SONGS LINCOLN LOVED

RESPECTFULLY DEDICATED TO
Linn Babcock, Esq.
THE
Silver Bell Waltz
Piano
BY
A. A. HOPKINS.
ROCHESTER:
Published by JOS. P. SHAW, No. 43 State St.

Oh! why should the spirit
of mortal be proud.
POEM BY
ABRAHAM LINCOLN
Music by
GEO. C. PEARSON.
BOSTON

GO · WORK · TO · DAY
YOUR
IN · MY · VINEYARD
MISSION.

BY

JOHN LAIR

With an Introduction by
William H. Townsend

DUELL, SLOAN AND PEARCE · NEW YORK
LITTLE, BROWN AND COMPANY · BOSTON

LIBRARY OF CONGRESS CATALOG CARD NO. 54-6876

FIRST EDITION

DUELL, SLOAN AND PEARCE—LITTLE, BROWN
BOOKS ARE PUBLISHED BY
LITTLE, BROWN AND COMPANY
IN ASSOCIATION WITH
DUELL, SLOAN & PEARCE, INC.

Published simultaneously in Canada
by Little, Brown & Company (Canada) Limited

PRINTED IN THE UNITED STATES OF AMERICA

THE BATTLE CRY OF FREEDOM BY Geo. F. Root.

Published by Root & Cady,
95 Clark Street,
CHICAGO.

To the memory of my mother
Belle Coffey Lair

ACKNOWLEDGMENTS

Throughout this book I have tried to give individual credit for help received in getting it together. I do, however, want to especially mention two noted Lincoln authorities, R. Gerald McMurty and William H. Townsend, for their very substantial aid. Mr. McMurtry, as Director of the Department of Lincolniana of Lincoln Memorial University, placed at my disposal their entire collection and was most helpful in the research. Mr. Townsend read over my book, furnished copies of the two Lincoln scripts appearing herein, and wrote the introduction for the book, for which I am grateful.

CONTENTS

INTRODUCTION

John Lair, the "Laird" of Renfro Valley, in the knob country of Eastern Kentucky, whose barn dance troupers on stage and radio are nationally known, has discovered an unplowed plot in the highly cultivated field of Lincolniana.

Born and reared in the Kentucky foothills, he heard from his earliest recollections the hymns and ballads that were sung in Abraham Lincoln's childhood and youth. Old favorites from Dupuy's hymnbook and *The Missouri Harmony* — and others like the tragic "Fair Ellender," the misfortunes of poor Lord Randall, the haunting melody of "Barbara Allen" and "Gentle Annie" and play-party songs like "Old Sister Phoebe" and "Skip-to-My-Lou."

Dennis Hanks, Lincoln's kinsman and boyhood companion, remembered that "Abe" liked what Mr. Lair, with commendable understatement, calls the "lustier" songs. Hanks, in his weird but picturesque spelling, undertakes to quote the leading lines of one of these: " 'the turbenturk [turbaned Turk] that Scorns the world and Struts a Bout with his whiskers curld for No other man but his-Self to see' — and all Such as this."

Lincoln's maturity brought an elevation in taste, but minstrel songs, especially dialect, still delighted him, as well as comic or "nonsense" rhymes set to music or rhythm. Perhaps his first preference, throughout his life, was what he called "little sad songs" — "Twenty Years Ago," "Rock Me to Sleep, Mother," and "Kathleen Mavourneen."

Years ago I remember seeing the original of a personal letter that a Civil War general, I believe it was Carl Schurz, the famous German-American, wrote to an intimate friend shortly after Chancellorsville in which he related the following incident. The General and Lincoln sat in one of the downstairs rooms of the White House gravely discussing that recent disaster to the Army of the Potomac, especially the losses and conduct of the 11th Corps that had borne the brunt of Jackson's onslaught. Twilight came and Lincoln waved aside the servant who came in to light the chandeliers. Observing a piano across the threshold of an adjoining room, the General got up, walked over and adjusted the stool, sat down and began to run his fingers over the ivory keyboard. Softly he played "Tenting Tonight on the Old Camp Ground" and other popular favorites, winding up with the poignant "Lorena." Throughout the impromptu concert, the President sat in the semi-darkness, relaxed and lost in reverie. When he had finished, Lincoln thanked him warmly and spoke of how deeply he always had been affected by music of a sentimental nature.

Mr. Lair has spent many years in collecting the hymns, ballads, and other songs of the nineteenth century and has traced many of them back to where they originated long before they were brought to the New World. His Old Music Library in his spacious residence at Renfro Valley is one of the largest now in private hands. Much of the author's time has been devoted to the music of the Lincoln period and to the songs that we know Lincoln liked and to those he must have heard since they were favorites of his day and generation. Mr. Lair's work is something new — impossible as it may seem — in collateral Lincolniana. As a contribution to genuine Americana, it will have even a wider appeal.

William H. Townsend

Lexington, Kentucky

FOREWORD

If an apology be needed for adding another volume to the many books which have been written about Abraham Lincoln, let it be that this one treats of a phase of his life and character but little noticed in other works. Herein is set forth his preference in music — the songs he knew and loved and sometimes tried to sing.

I can think of three people who, if they could come back to life and know that someone was seriously considering Abraham Lincoln's connection with any form of music, would be both amused and amazed. First would be Dennis Hanks, an older cousin with whom he grew up. Dennis, who was never one to give himself the worst of it in any comparison with his famous relative, talked freely and often of the songs they knew but would have us think of himself as the songbird of the Lincoln-Hanks group. He said that Abe wasn't much of a singer; couldn't even sing "Pore Old Ned," though he tried often enough. Next would be Billy Herndon, Lincoln's law partner, close friend, and self-confessed political counselor. When asked in later years by a Lincoln biographer if Mr. Lincoln could sing, he answered that question with another, inelegantly put but entirely conclusive, "Can a jackass whistle?" And last of the three would be Lincoln himself, who always declared in public that he could not sing, but who never gave up in private trying to do so.

The Lincolns probably were not a musical family. Abraham's cousin, Mordecai, son of an uncle by the same name, got all the talent in the family, Abe once said (he also got most of the property, it seems); according to the Reverend John W. Cunningham, his neighbor in Leitchfield, Kentucky, Mordecai was "a charming fiddler." The fiddle Mordecai played had been made by an old soldier of the Revolution, who whittled it out of sugartree wood with a cobbler's shoe knife. Mordecai, who was also a cobbler by trade, would sit on his porch at night and fiddle for the whole community to hear. Sometimes the wolves would hear and answer him from the darkness of the surrounding forest. Abraham once told a group of schoolchildren that as a boy he had played the jew's-harp, and a companion traveling with him during the Lincoln-Douglas debates recalls that one day Lincoln took a harmonica from his pocket and played on it as they rode along, saying, "This is my band. Douglas had a brass band at Peoria, but this will do for me." We cannot tell, of course, whether he was actually in the habit of playing the harmonica or if his shrewd, practical political sense seized upon this lowly musical instrument of the common people to identify himself with them, as opposed to Douglas's more spectacular appeal.

But regardless of the fact that Abraham Lincoln could not himself produce music he had a soul for its appreciation. He was a great lover of music, if not a lover of great music. He had no fondness for the classics but loved everything between the two extremes of early minstrel nonsense songs and the popular love songs of his later days. He was very responsive to music. His friends knew that certain sentimental ballads would mist his eyes with tears and throw him into a fit of deep melancholy, but they early learned that through the same medium which brought about this despondency he could also be freed from it. His banjo-thumping friend, Ward Hill Lamon, often said that when he saw

Lincoln in one of his depressed moods a lively and humorous song would instantly restore him to his wonted gaiety. So closely were Lincoln's moods associated with the songs he knew and loved that we may sometimes wonder if the mood produced the songs or the songs induced the mood.

But it is not the purpose of this book to deal in conclusions. The Lincoln student will draw his own and the casual reader will not be interested, anyway. It will have served its real purpose if it has brought together in one volume the simple songs which Abraham Lincoln, the great American, knew and loved. If they do not explain his greatness they may at least add something to our understanding of the poor boy who went from a backwoods cabin to the White House, yet never lost touch with those he passed along the way — never forgot the teachings, or the songs, of one of whom he was to say in later years, "All that I am or ever hope to be I owe to my Mother. God bless her!"

SONGS LINCOLN LOVED

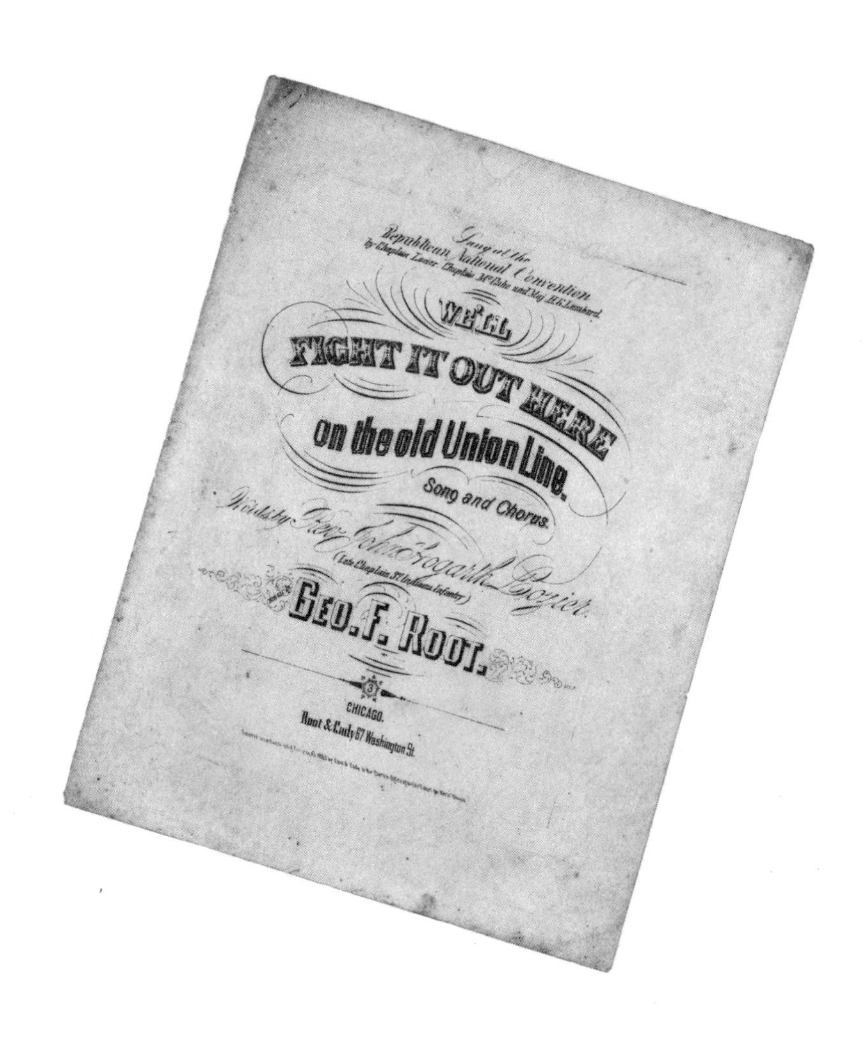

On a cold, snowy Sunday morning in February, at the low ebb of the year, when earth and sky and all between were leaden-gray in the frozen dawn, Tom and Nancy Lincoln's second child and first son was born. When he lifted his voice in that first fretful protest, old as the human race itself, against being ushered into this world of sorrow and woe, it must be admitted that he had seeming cause for complaint.

The early morning light, gleaming pewter-dull through the thin-scraped sheepskin stretched across the one window opening, showed him little to be proud of, and the mounting flames on the hearth as Thomas "chunked up" the fire and added a new 'fore stick were but little more revealing. There were the four mud-daubed walls of the pole cabin, the dirt floor and the rough stone fireplace, a home-made hickory chair or two, a corner bedstead of cleat-and-pole contrivance, the spider and skillet and oven for cooking — and little else besides.

The mother to whom he was snuggled close under the "kivers" and bearskins for body warmth, the stolid, slow-moving father who turned back the bed covering to peer at him, and the dark, round-faced, silent little girl his father brought to look at him were the family group he had come to join. While he grew to know deep love and affection for them, especially his mother, he was never to think of them as more than a second-rate family, and so designated his ancestry in his own brief autobiography in later years when he was beginning to attract nationwide attention. He lived out his life in this belief, learning very little of the sterling qualities of the family whose name he bore.

If the infant Lincoln had little to be proud of, let it be said in all justice that there was little reason at the time to feel that the world had gotten much the better of the bargain. Probably his cousin Dennis Hanks voiced the sentiments of those who came to see the new baby, when after briefly holding him in his arms he handed him back to Nancy saying, "A'nt, take him. He'll never come to much!" Newborn babies were not supposed to be beautiful, but there were those who allowed that "the Linkern baby" had "sorter overdone hit."

Tom had agreed that Nancy should have the naming of the new arrival and she called him after Tom's own father, Abraham. This Abraham Lincoln, or Linkhorn as some folks spelled it, had been a man to be proud of, although there have been those who hinted darkly that he had done very little for his country during the trying years of the Revolution. He was a captain of militia in Virginia but left scant record of anything he did in that capacity, except for some skirmishes with the Indian allies of the British redcoats. In this connection I am wondering if Lincoln historians have not overlooked something of interest in passing up the account of Mrs. Sarah Graham, who in 1780, as Sarah Spilman, daughter of Charles Spilman, was camped with the family in the vicinity of what is now Danville, Kentucky, near the pioneer station settled by my father's great-great-grandfather, William Lawrence. Mrs. Graham told in after years that while her family was camped there a man named Abraham Linkhorn was captured by the Indians and kept a prisoner about eighteen months. Her story was that he was on his way back to Virginia to bring in his family, having first come out to locate lands for settlement. Early entries indicate that he took up land in what was later Jefferson County, Kentucky, in 1780, but there seems to be no record of his family coming in before 1782, a lapse of time which may be explained by his detention among the Indians as related by Mrs. Graham. His troubles with the red men, however, were not over until he was shot down near his cabin in the wilderness by a skulking savage, while his youngest son, Thomas, Abe's father, looked on in childish bewilderment. The Lincoln family never tired of telling this story and how one of Tom's older brothers aimed the captain's rifle between the logs of the cabin and shot the Indian dead just as he was about to make off with little Thomas. So the baby was named for his grandfather, the Captain Abraham Lincoln who was a friend of the Boones and other early pioneers in the Dark and Bloody Ground, made darker by his own life's blood.

Abe Lincoln, it was said, did not have much "favorance" to his pappy's folks, but "tuck atter the Hankses," his mammy's side of the house. Nancy Hanks could not boast of such a father as Tom had had. In fact, it has been said that she never even knew his name, yet Abe always believed that she inherited from him the qualities of mind and character which were her heritage to her son. She was a woman of strange moods and given to frequent spells of sadness. She loved and sang sad songs — tragic ballads of Old World knights and ladies fair who lived and loved and died heroically. Most pioneer women shared with her this preference, and the songs they sang as they went about their drudging toil in their rude cabin homes had little of bright hope and blessed promise this side of the grave.

There was the ballad of Fair Ellender, with its gory triple tragedy; the ballad of Lord Randall, poisoned by his own sweetheart, tugged at the lonesome-hearted listeners who heard it; and the story of the Oxford Girl, told to music or in the singsong recitative fashion of those who could not sing, also spread its share of shuddering gloom.

As Nancy Lincoln held her baby boy to her thin breast and crooned into his sleepy senses the tragic words and wild, haunting, minor-key melodies that harmonized with her strange longings and the moods of dark despair she often knew, did she implant in his youthful heart the fatalistic premonition of a tragic death that always haunted him? As she sat with him and little Sarah on the doorstep of their cabin home, waiting for Tom to come home from the day's work or wanderings, did she sing to them these strange ballads of a faraway world and long-ago time which carried the mind of at least one of the children beyond the four walls of a wilderness cabin and inspired him to know something of the things beyond his narrow horizons? As she sometimes sang, soft and low, so as not to drown out the creek frogs and the katydids and the lonesome whippoorwills who made their music to the gathering dusk, did the boy Abe, the child of destiny, feel the same longings that had tugged at the heartstrings of his mother?

BARBARA ALLEN

All in the merry month of May,
When green buds they were swelling,
Sweet William on his deathbed lay
For the love of Barbara Allen.

He sent his servant to the town,
To the place where she was dwelling,
Saying, "Hasten away and come with me,
If your name be Barbara Allen."

It is claimed that Lincoln stated in after years that "Barbara Allen" was his mother's favorite song. If so, then it must have been his childhood's favorite, too, because it would have been the one he heard most often and remembered best. Here it is, as still remembered and sung in the Kentucky hill country where he heard it as a child. The illustration used is reproduced from an old woodcut embellishing the penny ballad of "Barbara Allen's Cruelty," hawked about the foggy streets of London long before the ancestors of the Lincoln and Hanks families had set sail from Old England to the New World that was to become America.

Then slowly, slowly she got up
And slowly she came nigh him,
And all the words she would speak to him,
"Young man, I think you're dying."

"O, yes, I'm sick and very sick
And death is on me dwelling.
No better, no better I never will be
If I can't have Barbara Allen."

"Do you remember in yonder town
When you were at the tavern,
You drank a toast to the ladies all around
But slighted Barbara Allen?"

"O, yes, I remember in yonder town
When I was at the tavern
I gave a toast to the ladies all around,
But my heart to Barbara Allen."

As she was on her highway home
She spied his corpse a-coming;
"Set down, set down this corpse of clay
That I may look upon him."

The more she looked, the more she wept
Till she fell to the ground, a-crying,
"O, pick me up and carry me home,
For I am now a-dying.

"O, Father, O, Father, go dig my grave;
Go dig it long and narrow.
Sweet William died for me today,
I'll die for him tomorrow."

Upon her grave there grew a red rose.
On William's grave grew a briar.
They twined and they twined in a true-lover's knot,
And the rose grew around the briar.

Another old song Nancy Lincoln sang to little Sarah and Abraham in the long evenings before a blazing hearth was "William Riley." Sometimes the children tried to join her in the singing of certain old favorites. With some songs that was easy. A sort of singsong recital of the words would serve well enough for those who couldn't carry a tune, but this wouldn't do with a song like "William Riley." It had to be just right or you could get lost mighty easy.

Here it is, with the music to show how it really should be sung.

WILLIAM RILEY

Come all young men and maidens and hark to what I tell
Of bold young William Riley and what to him befell.
With some rich merchant's daughter he quickly rode away.
O'er hills and highest mountains they rode both night and day.

Her father followed after with all his chosen band,
And soon did overtake them and Riley bid to stand.
'Twas then they overbore him and brought him to the ground
And took him off to prison in chains and fetters bound.

They cast him in a dungeon that was both dark and deep
And placed a guard around him his body for to keep,
The while the merchant's daughter she did both weep and wail
To think of William Riley confinèd in the jail.

And there they did confine him until the court was met
And by the judge and jury his trial day was set.
'Twas early in the morning upon that fatal day
The jailor came, stepped up to him, and unto him did say:

"Now rise up, William Riley, you must appear this day.
The lady's oath will hang you, or else will set you free."
"If this be so," said Riley, "some hope begins to dawn,
For I never can be injured by my pretty Colleen Bawn."

He said unto the jury, "From Ballahone I came.
I am the son of Riley, and William is my name.
I am no thief nor robber, nor murder have I done.
My only crime was roving with my pretty Colleen Bawn."

And then up stepped the counselor who stood attentive by;
"Gentlemen of the jury, on justice we rely.
To hang a man for loving, foul murder seems to me,
So spare the life of Riley and let him banished be."

"Oh, stop!" cried her old father. "He stol'd her golden rings,
Gold watch and diamond buckles and many costly things.
I gave them to my daughter, they cost a thousand pound;
When Riley was o'ertaken these things with him were found."

Then up stepped this young maiden poor William's life to save;
"All that you found on Riley to him I freely gave,
But if you have them, Riley, return them now to me."
"I will," said William Riley, "and that most willingly."

They bound poor William Riley and took him straight away,
Chained up with many others, all bound for Botany Bay.
The rich old merchant's daughter, she cried in wildest grief,
"For me poor William Riley is treated like a thief!"

From his eighth to his twenty-first year, young Abraham Lincoln was growing up on the Indiana frontier, under conditions generally more primitive than the Lincoln and Hanks families had known in the longer-settled communities from which they had been lured by the promise of cheap, new farmlands north of the broad Ohio. Dennis Hanks has told of the songs he and Lincoln knew and which he, at least, sang. Dennis, with commendable modesty, said he would not even name many of the "field" songs they knew — rough-humored ditties not "fitten" to be sung around the house. He confined his list largely to hymns, although he adds that hymn-singing didn't exactly suit Abe, who seemed to have a bent for the lustier songs he had learned in the cornfields and along the river.

Dennis maintains that the old Dupuy (he spells it Dupree) hymnbook was the only one they knew anything about, mentioning it as the book used by the old Presbyterian Baptists in 1820. Elder Stark Dupuy, compiler of this book, *Hymns and Spiritual Songs,* was a noted early-day Baptist minister in Kentucky and Tennessee. His hymnbook was first published at Louisville, Kentucky, in 1818. It ran into twenty-two editions during his own lifetime, selling more than one hundred thousand copies, chiefly in the Western and Southern states. The earliest copy in my Old Music Library at Renfro Valley, Kentucky, is dated 1826.

Another of Lincoln's youthful companions was David Turnham. In a letter to William H. Herndon, in reply to Mr. Herndon's letter of inquiry on the subject, Turnham lists additional hymns they sang. This letter, reproduced here, is from the original manuscript which is now in posession of William H. Townsend. It has not hitherto been published.

Dale Ind Dec 30 - 65
Mr Herendon
Dear sir

yours of the 16th inst is
recieved. I will Cherfully
Comply with your request
so far as I Can.
as to the songs sung in those
days by the young folks. I
have forgotten all except pious
songs, of those I will give
you a few . and I will Commence
with one which Abe ~~one~~ asked
me to sing for his father. I
Complyed and the old Jentleman
wold have me sing it often
afterward
it Commenced thus
1. There was a Romish lady
brought up in popery

the Hymns used was Dr Watts &
Dupuys Hymns
I will name a few of the hymns
sung in Church

Am I a soldier of the Cross
a follower of the lamb

How tedious and tastless the hours
when Jesus no longer I se

there is a fountain filled with blood
Drawn from Immanuels veins

Alas and did my Savier bleed
and did my soverin die

Jesus my all to heaven is gone
he whome I fixed my hopes upon

Dear friend,
I have tried to answer

your questions as well as I can
if there is any thing more that
I can be of any service to you
I will gladly serve you

I would like to know
if you ever Got that old
law book, it is the revised
statute of 1824
if you have not, and wish it
I will try to git it and send
it to you
I wish you success with
your Book

yours respectfully

D Turnham

All of the hymns associated with Lincoln's youth are found in the Dupuy hymnal, but only the words are given, as was the general custom in hymnbooks of that era. I have found the music to all of them in either *The Missouri Harmony,* used by the Lincolns and their neighbors in the Little Pigeon church, or in *Musica Sacra,* or in *The Sacred Harp.*

NINETY-FIFTH
When I can read my title clear To mansions in the skies, I'll bid farewell to ev'ry fear, And wipe my weeping eyes.
BLENDON
Jesus, my all, to heav'n is gone, He whom I fix my hopes upon; His track I see, and I'll pursue The narrow way till him I view.
BLEEDING SAVIOUR
A las! and did my Saviour bleed, And did my Sovereign die? Would he de - vote that sacred head For such a worm as I?
BOUND FOR CANAAN
O when shall I see Jesus, And reign with him above?
And from the flowing fountain, Drink everlasting love?
I'm on my way to Canaan, I'm on my way to Canaan, I'm on my way to Canaan, To the New Jerusalem
NEW MONMOUTH
Come thou fount of ev'ry blessing, Tune my heart to sing thy grace; Streams of mercy, never ceasing, Call for songs of loudest praise.

David Turnham's inclusion of "The Romish Lady" is substantiated by Dennis Hanks, who says it was a favorite of Abe's. At Abe's insistence young Turnham sang it for Thomas Lincoln also, and Abe and his father agreed it was the best of the lot. While it certainly could not be classed as a hymn I feel that, as a matter of historical interest, it should be included here.

THE ROMISH LADY

There was a Romish lady, brought up in popery,
Her mother always taught her the priests she must obey.
"O pardon me, dear Mother, I humbly pray thee now
But unto the false idols I can no longer bow."

Assisted by her handmaid a Bible she concealed
And there she gained instruction, till God his love revealed.
No more herself she prostrates to pictures decked with gold;
But soon she was betrayed and her Bible from her stole.

With grief and great vexation her mother straight did go
To inform the Roman Clergy the cause of all her woe.
The priests were soon assembled and for the maid did call,
And forced her in the dungeon to fright her soul withal.

The more they sought to fright her, the more she did endure:
Although her age was tender, her faith was strong and sure.
The chains of gold so costly they from this lady took,
And she, with all her spirit, the pride of life forsook.

Before the pope they brought her in hopes of her return,
And there she was condemnèd in horrid flames to burn.
Before the place of torment they brought her speedily;
With hands upraised to heaven she then agreed to die.

There being many ladies assembled at that place,
She raised her eyes to heaven and begged supplying grace.
"Weep not, ye tender ladies, shed not a tear for me;
While my poor body's burning, my soul the Lord shall see.

"Yourselves you need to pity, and Zion's deep decay;
Dear ladies, turn to Jesus, no longer make delay."
In comes her raging mother, her daughter to behold,
And in her hand she brought her the pictures decked with gold.

"O, take from me those idols, remove them from my sight;
Restore to me my Bible, wherein I take delight.
Alas! my aged mother, why on my ruin bent?
'Twas you that did betray me, but I am innocent.

"Tormentors, use your pleasure, and do as you think best;
I hope my blessed Jesus will take my soul to rest."
Soon as these words were spoken, up steps the man of death,
And kindled up the fire to stop her mortal breath.

Instead of golden bracelets, with chains they bound her fast;
She cried: "My God, give power, now must I die at last.
With Jesus and his angels I shall forever dwell;
God pardon priests and people, and so I bid farewell!"

Although Lincoln showed but little interest in hymns in his more youthful days, they came to mean more to him as he grew older. Captain Gilbert Greene relates that in the beginning years of Lincoln's law practice he once accompanied Lincoln on a professional trip to draw up the will of an old farm woman who was on her deathbed. After the legal business had been attended to she entered into conversation with young Lincoln, during which she asked him to read to her from the Bible. One of the family brought her Bible to him. He took it in his hands but did not open it, quoting from memory the Twenty-third Psalm and going on into the fourteenth chapter of John. After this he offered a few more selected Bible quotations and recited the words of various hymns, closing with the last verse of "Rock of Ages."

While I draw this fleeting breath,
When mine eyelids close in death,
When I soar to worlds unknown,
See Thee on Thy judgment throne,
Rock of Ages, cleft for me,
Let me hide myself in Thee.

Another hymn Abraham Lincoln never forgot I have also found in my copy of the Dupuy hymnbook, finding the tune to which it was sung in an early Methodist hymnal. Under the sobering title of "Death," its opening lines, often given as the title, prepare us for what is to follow.

Carl Sandburg and other Lincoln authorities have said that this was the hymn Ann Rutledge sang to Lincoln during the happy days of their courtship, which ended all too soon in her untimely death. They could have sung it together on quiet summer evenings as they sat on the front porch and watched a misty moon come up above the Sangamon. Or perhaps, thrilled with their nearness to each other, they held their hymnbook together when they attended church and lifted their voices with those of the congregation as they sang, "Vain man, thy fond pursuits forbear. Reflect, thine end is nigh!" For one of them the end was indeed nigh. There is a legend that Ann sang this song to Abe as he sat for the last time by her sickbed a little while before she died.

Lincoln historians continue to debate inconclusively over the question of whether or not there was anything to the Ann Rutledge story. Some have pointed out that soon after her death he was paying court to a Kentucky visitor, Miss Mary Owens, and that he could not have been so deeply in love with Ann or so greatly grieved at her death. Those who better understand Lincoln's intense nature and the worshipful awe in which he, like so many plain, awkward, unattractive men, held all women can well believe that he was hard hit by the tragedy of Ann Rutledge's death. Up to that time she was the most desirable and attractive girl to pay much attention to the shy backwoods youth, who had had very little experience with the opposite sex. He had seen how popular she was with the eligible men of the community — how at least one friendship and business association had been broken up by rivalry for her hand — and when the field was unexpectedly cleared for him by the removal from the scene, under unflattering circumstances, of her favored suitor he pressed his own suit and was successful. To win such a prize only to lose her to the dark rival, Death, might well have seemed to him more than he could bear, and it is altogether probable that he did sink into a fit of despondency and despair bordering on temporary insanity. He freely admitted this to his friends, and years later when Isaac Cogdale visited him in the White House he told him, in answer to Cogdale's rather prying and personal questions, that he had indeed been in love with Ann Rutledge — that she was his first real love and that he had never forgotten her. He also admitted that he had "run a little wild" at her death. Is there any reason for believing that he was not telling the truth? In the years that followed, other loves came into his life. He married and raised a family, to which he was indulgently devoted, and intimate friends agreed that he was always faithful to his marriage vows, but we may well believe that Ann Rutledge, first love of his young heart, never faded from his memory.

Soon after her death a friend gave him a copy of the poem "Mortality," and as long as he lived it was his declared favorite. Its opening lines — "Oh, why should the spirit of mortal be proud?" — were so much like "Vain man, thy fond pursuits forbear!" of their favorite hymn that the poem may have seemed to him a sequel to the song associated in his memory with Ann and her early death. He was also very fond of Holmes's poem "The Last Leaf," and his friends thought it was of Ann Rutledge he was thinking when he recited from the poem these lines forever underscored in his heart:

The mossy marbles rest
On the lips that he has pressed
In their bloom,
And the names he loved to hear
Have been carved for many a year
On the tomb.

There was the day when an anguished mother came to the White House to plead for the release of her son from prison. As President Lincoln sat listening to her in his usual courteous and patient manner, her young daughter, who had accompanied her on the call, wandered over to the piano in the room and began softly to play and sing Foster's "Gentle Annie," beginning:

Thou wilt come no more, gentle Annie,
Like a flower thy spirit did depart;
Thou art gone, alas! like the many
That have bloomed in the summer of my heart.

During the singing of the song the President got up and walked over to a window, where he stood looking out until the song was finished. Then with a look of sadness on his furrowed face he turned back to his caller and immediately granted her request. As the joyful mother and daughter hurried from the room with the good news, the last lines of the song may have still echoed in his heart:

Shall we never more behold thee;
Never hear thy winning voice again —
When the Spring time comes, gentle Annie,
When the wild flowers are scattered o'er the plain?

Perhaps he was thinking of the gentle Annie of his own youth and that long-ago spring along the Sangamon when they had strolled among "the wild flowers scattered o'er the plain" and she had lifted up her voice in the hymn he loved because she sang it — "Vain man, thy fond pursuits forbear."

DEATH

Vain man, thy fond pursuits forbear;
Reflect! thy end is nigh.
Death, at the fartherest, can't be far;
Repent, before thou die.

Reflect; thou hast a soul to save;
Thy sins, how high they mount!
What are thy hopes beyond the grave?
How stands that dark account?

Death enters, and there's no defence;
His time there's none can tell;
He'll in a moment call thee hence
To Heaven or to Hell.

Thy flesh, perhaps thy chiefest care,
Shall crawling worms consume.
But, ah! destruction ends not there;
Sin kills beyond the tomb.

Today the gospel calls — today!
Sinners, it speaks to you;
Let every one forsake his way
And mercy will ensue.

Rich mercy, dearly bought with blood,
How vile soe'er ye be;
Abundant pardon, peace with God,
All giv'n entirely free.

GENTLE ANNIE.

CHORUS.
Shall we ne_ver more be_hold thee; ne_ver hear thy winning voice a_
gain When the Spring time comes, gen_tle Annie, When the
wild flowers are scattered o'er the plain?

In an old hymnal, *Select Melodies,* compiled by William Hunter and published by the Methodist Book Concern at Cincinnati, Ohio, is the hymn "Pilgrim Stranger." On the margin of the page is this handwritten notation by the owner, Elizabeth Funk: *Lincoln heard Ann Rutledge sing this song before he fell in love with her.* Laura J. Funk, a daughter-in-law of Elizabeth Funk, showed me this book in 1934. She was eighty-nine years old at that time. She was able to enlarge upon the information contained in the notation, telling me that Elizabeth Funk had often told her the story of how Abraham Lincoln, while walking in the woods near New Salem, had heard a fresh young voice singing, "I'm a pilgrim, I'm a stranger." The singer was hidden from his view and he did not know her identity. Sitting in church the following Sunday, listening to the hymns being sung, he was delighted to recognize the voice he had heard in the forest a few days before. He learned that the girl was Ann Mays Rutledge, who, like himself, had moved to Indiana from Kentucky. This was the first time he ever saw her.

Since this copy of *Select Melodies* was published in 1855, several years after Ann's death, it is not, of course, claimed that she had learned the hymn from this book. In the introductory announcement in the book it was stated that it contained many numbers in common use not found in any standard church hymnbook. I have mislaid my own copy of *Select Melodies* and that of Mrs. Funk is not now available, but to the best of my recollection the hymn here given, which is from *The Glory,* published by John Church and Company, Cincinnati, Ohio, in 1872, is the same as the one in *Select Melodies.* I have also found it in hymnbooks printed as early as 1848, so if this is the hymn under discussion, then the compilers of *Select Melodies* may have erred in stating that hymns in their book had not previously been published — an error quite common to the publishers of such books in that day.

PILGRIM STRANGER

3.

There's the city to which I journey;
My Redeemer, my Redeemer is its light!
There is no sorrow, nor any sighing,
Nor any tears there, nor any dying!
I'm a pilgrim, and I'm a stranger,
I can tarry, I can tarry but a night.

4.

Farewell, neighbors, with tears I've warned you,
I must leave you, I must leave you and be gone!
With this your portion, your heart's desire,
Why will you perish in raging fire!
I'm a pilgrim, and I'm a stranger,
I can tarry, I can tarry but a night.

5.

Father, mother and sister, brother!
If you will not journey with me I must go!
Now since your vain hopes you will thus cherish,
Should I too linger and with you perish?
I'm a pilgrim, and I'm a stranger,
I can tarry, I can tarry but a night.

6.

Farewell, dreary earth, by sin so blighted,
In immortal beauty soon you'll be arrayed!
He who has formed thee, will soon restore thee,
And then thy dread curse shall never more be: —
I'm a pilgrim, and I'm a stranger,
Till thy rest shall end the weary pilgrim's night!

On January 29, 1865, at a mass meeting held in the hall of the House of Representatives and presided over by Secretary Seward, Philip Phillips, noted singing evangelist and hymnbook compiler, appeared on the musical part of the program, singing the stirring hymn "Your Mission." President Lincoln was so much impressed with this hymn that he sent up a note asking that before the meeting closed Mr. Phillips be asked to repeat it, with the stipulation that his own identity in connection with the request be withheld.

"Your Mission" is here reproduced from an old hymnal, *The Singing Pilgrim,* published by Philip Phillips and Company, 1866, New York and Cincinnati, and lent to me for this compilation by Mrs. William Roper of Hillsboro, Tennessee.

GO WORK TO-DAY IN MY VINEYARD

YOUR MISSION

THE words of this truly beautiful song were written by Mrs. Ellen H. Gates. The music will be found on page 90, "Musical Leaves," as sung by Philip Phillips at the great Anniversaries of the U. S. Christian Commission in New York, Philadelphia, Washington, Cincinnati, Chicago, St. Louis, and many other places.

When our lamented President Lincoln heard Mr. Phillips sing it at the Hall of Representatives in Washington, Feb. 29, 1865, he was overcome with emotion, and sent up the following written request (facsimile) to Hon. Wm. H. Seward, Chairman, for its repetition:

"Near the close let us have "Your Mission" repeated by Mr Phillips Dont say I called for it A. Lincoln

Composed by S. M. Grannis.

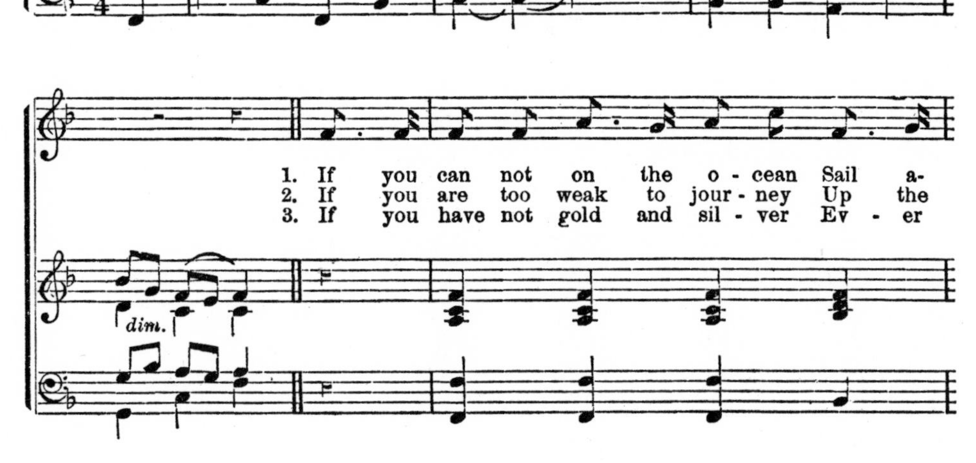

4 If you can not in the conflict
Prove yourself a soldier true,
If, where fire and smoke are thickest,
There's no work for you to do;
When the battlefield is silent,
You can go with careful tread,
You can bear away the wounded,
You can cover up the dead.

5 Do not, then, stand idly waiting,
For some greater work to do;
Fortune is a lazy goddess,
She will never come to you.
Go and toil in any vineyard,
Do not fear to do or dare,
If you want a field of labor,
You can find it any where.

THE PRESIDENT'S HYMN.

In response to the Proclamation of the President of the United States, recommending a General Thanksgiving on November 26, 1863. When the dedication was proposed to the President, he answered, "Let it be so called."

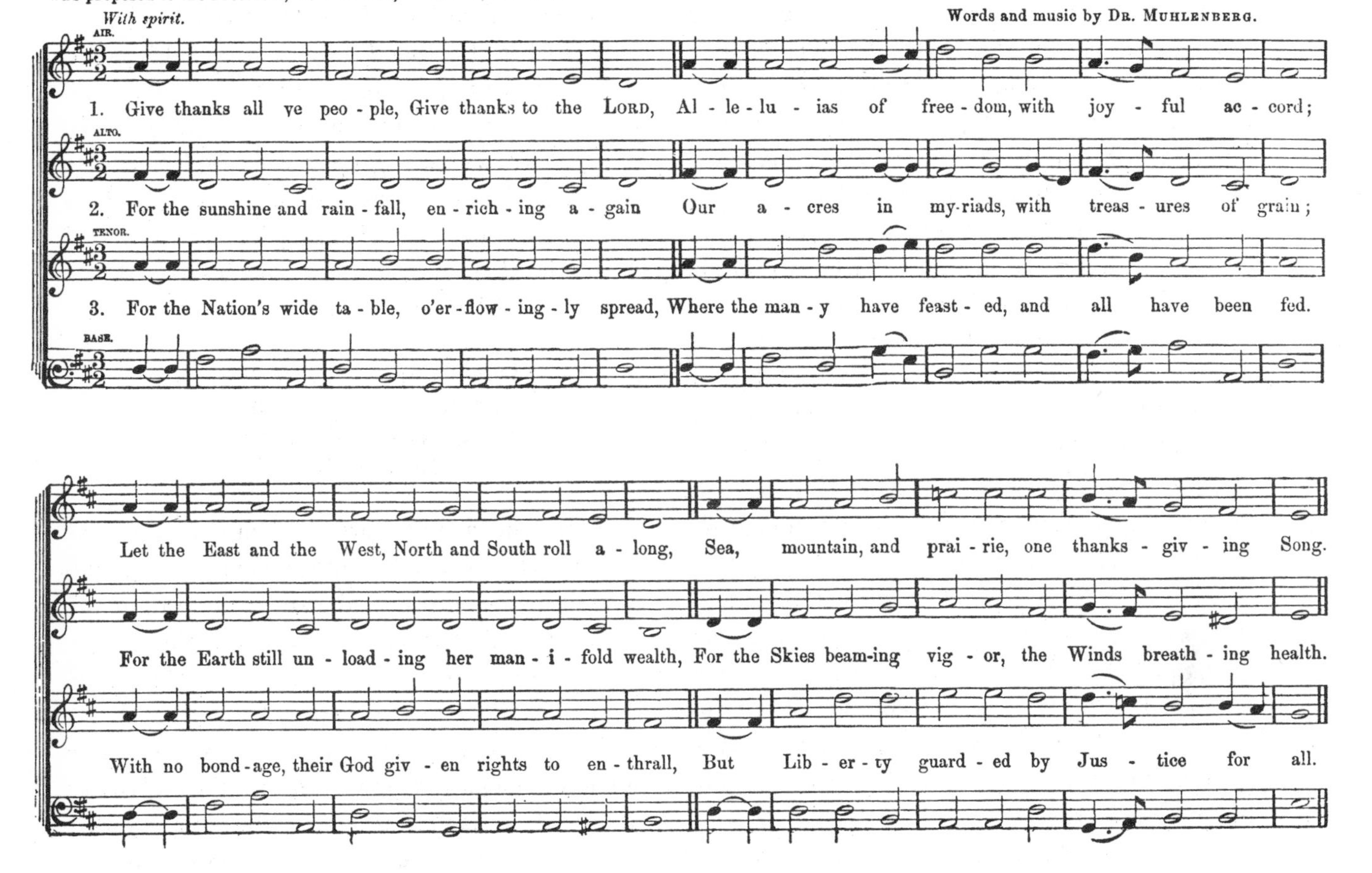

4. In the realms of the Anvil, the Loom, and the Plow,
Whose the mines and the fields, to Him gratefully bow:
His the flocks and the herds, sing ye hill-sides and vales:
On His ocean domains chant His name with the gales.
Give thanks, &c.

5. Of commerce and traffic, ye princes, behold
Your riches from Him whose the silver and gold,
Happier children of Labor, true lords of the soil,
Bless the Great Master Workman, who blesseth your toil.
Give thanks, &c.

6. Brave men of our forces, life-guard of our coasts,
To your Leader be loyal, Jehovah of Hosts:
Glow the Stripes and the Stars aye with victory bright,
Reflecting His glory—He crowneth the Right.
Give thanks, &c.

7. Nor shall ye through our borders, ye stricken of heart,
Only wailing your dead, in the joy have no part:
God's solace be yours, and for you there shall flow
All that honor and sympathy's gifts can bestow.
Give thanks, &c.

8. In the domes of Messiah, ye worshipping throngs,
Solemn litanies mingle with jubilant songs;
The Ruler of Nations beseeching to spare,
And our Empire still keep the Elect of His care.
Give thanks, &c.

9. Our guilt and transgressions remember no more;
Peace, Lord! righteous Peace, of Thy gift we implore;
And the banner of Union, restored by Thy hand,
Be the Banner of Freedom o'er all in the land.
And the Banner of Union, &c.

At sixteen, Lincoln was six feet in height, long, thin, leggy, gawky. He went to all community gatherings — logrollings, grubbings, corn shuckings. His keen, droll wit and unfailing good humor made him a general favorite everywhere. Quite at ease with men and boys, he was shy in the presence of girls. Not very fond of them, thought Mrs. Allen Gentry. "Backward in the presence of girls," said David Turnham.

Of course, it cannot be doubted that Lincoln was acutely aware that he was too tall for his age, that his feet and hands were too big, his arms and body too thin for romantic appeal. And yet the girls who knew him well liked him, because, as one of them said, he was "friendly though not as sociable as he ought to be."

Katie Roby liked him. He was about seventeen, she fifteen, when they attended school together. He helped her with her lessons, but lost out when he started telling her that the sun did not rise and set, but that the world itself turned around. Katie thought that was silly — and that Abe was silly for talking that way.

There were other girls. In after years, when he became famous, there were middle-aged women in plenty to boast to their children that they were once Abraham Lincoln's sweethearts, basing the claim on nothing more definite than having played kissing games with him at a party, or having him walk home with them from "protracted meetin'."

At the neighborhood social affairs and "getherin's," Abe was apt to forget that he couldn't sing and would offer his version of "Legacy," or some doggerel of his own, generally a parody on some song well known to his listeners. One of these was to the tune "Auld Lang Syne" and expressed the political leanings of Abe and his friends. It was thought that he was the author of the words:

> Let old acquaintance be forgot
> And never brought to mind.
> May Jackson be our President
> And Adams left behind.

Again, he would start out with all patriotic fervor, "Hail, Columbia, happy land!"; then, with a rapid change of pace and manner, would sing the pay-off line, probably his own, "If you ain't drunk, then I'll be damned!" This one never failed to get the laugh he wanted to hear.

One song that struck Abe's fancy as being quite suitable for a party song was the one Dennis Hanks identified in later years as "The Turbenturk." Actually its title was "None Can Love Like an Irishman." It is given here as taken from my copy of the *Universal Songster, or Museum of Mirth,* published at London, England, by George Routledge and Sons. I have heard the song sung to the tune accompanying it here. There may be others.

NONE CAN LOVE LIKE AN IRISHMAN

The turban'd Turk, who scorns the world,
May strut about with his whiskers curled,
Keep a hundred wives under lock and key
For nobody else but himself to see;
Yet long may he pray with his Alcoran
Before he can love like an Irishman.

The gay Monsieur, a slave no more,
The solemn Don, the soft Signor,
The Dutch Mynheer, so full of pride,
The Russian, Prussian, Swede beside —
They all may do whate'er they can,
But they'll never love like an Irishman.

The London folks themselves beguile,
And think they please in a capital style;
Yet let them ask, as they cross the street,
Of any young virgin they happen to meet,
And I know she'll say, from behind her fan,
That there's none can love like an Irishman.

One of the party songs, or show pieces, which Dennis Hanks says Lincoln often found useful, was "Legacy," with words by Thomas Moore and the tune of an old Irish drinking song. Neither the words nor the tune made "Legacy" a fit companion for the hymns Allen Garden had gathered for his *Missouri Harmony,* but there it was, among its betters. It was even less fit to be heard in polite company after Abe, the prankster, got through with it. By so simple a change as substituting the words "old gray" for "the red grape" in the original lyrics, he was able, when he sang this song at parties and gatherings, at one stroke to throw the girls into giggling confusion and the boys into uncontrolled hilarity.

Carl Sandburg, in his *American Songbag,* gives "Legacy" as it appeared in *The Missouri Harmony,* which he says was published in 1808. However, I have never been able to come across an earlier edition of *The Missouri Harmony* than the one published by Morgan and Sanxy, of Cincinnati, Ohio, for the compiler, Allen Garden. Dr. William E. Barton, in his *Life of Lincoln,* states that he has a copy of *The Missouri Harmony,* the 1827 edition, and that it does not contain "Legacy." He states that the Rutledge family copy of this well-known hymnbook was published in 1844 — after Ann's death — and that "Legacy" appears in it, but in no earlier edition. His contention is that Abe and Ann could not have sung from any copy of *The Missouri Harmony* in which "Legacy" appeared. He is incorrect in this assumption, as my own copy of *The Missouri Harmony,* printed in 1834, does include this number. It is altogether likely that it was in still earlier editions of the same book. There is no reasonable ground for assuming that the 1844 copy in the possession of the Rutledge family years later was the only one they owned, or that some other branch of the family, or neighbor, might not have owned the copy from which Abe and Ann sang.

Dr. Barton was qualified above all other biographers to write of Lincoln and the part music played in his life. He was well versed in the folk music of earlier days and was, generally speaking, a painstaking student and historian. However, he was not so careful in running down dates and facts in connection with the music he mentions. For instance, he states that at the wedding of Thomas Lincoln and Nancy Hanks the fiddlers played, among other tunes, "Turkey in the Straw." The wedding took place in 1806. I have found no definite trace of this tune before 1815 — and then it was known as "Old Zip Coon," and it continued to be known under that title for several years thereafter.

Here is "Legacy," as found in my 1834 copy of *The Missouri Harmony.*

LEGACY

Young Abe Lincoln made a welcome hand at logrollings, house raisings, and other community projects calling for a willing spirit and a strong back. It was said of him that he could sink an ax deeper in a tree at a single stroke than any other man in Indiana. No doubt he was an equally proficient — and much more willing — participant in such social activities as bean stringings, apple cuttings, and corn shuckings, generally held in the evening to combine business with pleasure.

It has been said that he was not above the innocent trickery of carrying a red ear of corn in his pocket when he attended a corn shucking (husking bee, it was called in some places), to be slipped in among the other ears of corn and triumphantly produced at the proper time. Maybe that was the way he got to kiss Green Taylor's girl at one of these affairs. Anyway, Green must have thought so, for he rashly provoked a fight with Abe, with humiliating results to himself.

Dr. Barton, in his book *The Women Lincoln Loved,* tells how Abe accompanied Caroline Meeker to a neighborhood corn shucking following the winning of his first lawsuit, tried before her uncle, Squire Pate. Caroline, living as a member of the squire's household at the time, had become interested in young Lincoln as she listened to the trial of the suit brought against him for illegally operating a ferry. At the corn shucking which they later attended, two Negro slave musicians sang and played "Who Laid de Rail?" as given here.

WHO LAID DE RAIL?

Hit's a mighty dry year when de crab grass fail,
O,ro,ro,ro, who laid de rail?
Hit's a mighty dark night when de nigger turn pale,
De big-foot nigger dat laid de rail.

CHORUS:
O,ro,ro,ro, who laid de rail?
Show me de nigger dat laid de rail!

I'll hit him wid de hoe and I'll hit him wid de flail,
O,ro,ro,ro, who laid de rail?
I'll tro him thu de air like de buzzard do sail,
De big-foot nigger dat laid de rail.

Hit's might po' shuckin' when de red ear fail,
O,ro,ro,ro, who laid de rail?
De big-foot nigger dat kiss my gal
He hid dat red ear under de rail.

A popular form of entertainment for the long winter evenings in Indiana was the play-party. This was sort of a modified square dance where voices were used to furnish the music when a fiddler was not available or if the religious scruples of the household did not permit the fiddle's use. There were good, honest folk who subscribed to the belief that "The devil lives in a fiddle," but who did not object to dancing so long as the music was vocal only. At such play-parties nobody sang any louder, stomped the rough puncheon floor any harder, or swung the bright-eyed girls in linsey-woolsey any higher than big, lanky, awkward Abe Lincoln.

"Skip-to-My-Lou" was a popular play-party game in the Indiana days of Lincoln's youth. Strangely enough, its tune was from an old English hymn, "Give Up the World," as I learned recently from R. Cheyne-Stout. No one to my knowledge has been able to come up with any reasonable suggestion as to what the words of the title mean.

To play "Skip-to-My-Lou," young folks paired off and took up their positions at random about the room, leaving enough space in the center for the operations of the "stealer," a young man without a partner and anxious to remedy the situation. The crowd then went into the singing of the song,

Oh, mouse in the buttermilk,
Skip-to-my-Lou,
Mouse in the buttermilk,
Skip-to-my-Lou,
Mouse in the buttermilk,
Skip-to-my-Lou,
Skip-to-my-Lou, my darling.

She's gone again,
What shall I do,
She's gone again,
What shall I do,
She's gone again,
What shall I do,
Skip-to-my-Lou, my darling.

I'll get me another one
Prettier 'n you,
I'll get me another one
Prettier 'n you,
Pretty as a redbird,
Prettier, too,
Skip-to-my-Lou, my darling.

If I can't get a redbird
A bluebird 'll do,
If I can't get a redbird
A bluebird 'll do,
If I can't get a redbird
A bluebird 'll do,
Skip-to-my-Lou, my darling.

If I had a pistol
I'd shoot you,
If I had a pistol
I'd shoot you,
If I had a pistol
I'd shoot you,
Skip-to-my-Lou, my darling.

I'm going stealing,
Skip-to-my-Lou,
I'm going stealing,
Skip-to-my-Lou,
I'm going stealing,
Skip-to-my-Lou,
Skip-to-my-Lou, my darling.

You shan't keep her,
Dogged if you do,
You shan't keep her,
Dogged if you do,
You shan't keep her,
Dogged if you do,
Skip-to-my-Lou, my darling.

My wife's skipped,
And I'll skip, too,
My wife's skipped,
And I'll skip, too,
My wife's skipped,
And I'll skip, too,
Skip-to-my-Lou, my darling.

Stand there, Bigfoot,
Don't know what to do,
Stand there, Bigfoot,
Don't know what to do,
Stand there, Bigfoot,
Don't know what to do,
Skip-to-my-Lou, my darling.

keeping time with hands and feet, as the "stealer" skipped about the room to select the girl he would steal — often, for purposes of concealment of his true preference, the very one he didn't want. After he had skipped away with her it became the pleasant duty of her partner, thus bereaved, to skip about and steal somebody else's girl as the group clapped their hands and sang an appropriate verse of "Skip-to-My-Lou." The very nature of the proceedings invited improvisation, and he who could come up unexpectedly with a new verse expressive of his feelings at the moment was considered "quite a card."

Lincoln's favorite play-party game was "Old Sister Phoebe." To play it, any number of boys and girls, odd or even, joined hands and circled to the left around one girl in the center of the ring — the "Old Sister Phoebe" of the song. She held in her hand the hat, or coonskin cap, of one of the boys, and while the circle moved around, she carefully considered on whom to bestow her favor, as set forth in the first and second lines of the second verse. The blissful ordeal over, she could join in the anonymity of the circle while the young man she had honored now took his place in the center to crown the young lady of his choice with the same hat and in the same manner. This could go on and on for hours — and usually did.

OLD SISTER PHOEBE

Old Sister Phoebe, how happy were we
The day we sat under the juniper tree.
    The juniper tree, hi ho, hi ho!
    The juniper tree, hi ho!

Place this hat on your head, it will keep your head warm,
And take a sweet kiss, it will do you no harm,
    But a great deal of good, I know, I know;
    A great deal of good, I know.

Old Sister Phoebe, how happy were we
The day we sat under the juniper tree.
    Now around and around we go, we go;
    Around and around we go.

Mrs. Elizabeth Crawford, near neighbor and close friend of the Lincolns in Indiana, remembered that when Abe was seventeen years old he wrote a song to be sung at the wedding of his sister Sarah and Aaron Grigsby. It was called "Adam and Eve's Wedding Song." The neighbors all thought it was pretty good but they probably laughed good-naturedly at Abe's attempt to sing it in his high-pitched, unmusical voice. He had been writing poetry and making up songs since he was about twelve years old, so nobody was surprised at his writing a special song for such a special occasion. Mrs. Crawford recalled that she never heard anyone else except the Lincoln family sing it.

The wedding at which "Adam and Eve's Wedding Song" was presented was in 1826. Lincoln's supposed authorship of the song was not questioned for one hundred and two years. Early Lincoln biographers accepted Mrs. Crawford's story and it was not until 1928 that any doubt was raised. In that year Professor Charles Garrett Vannest, of Harris Teachers College, St. Louis, Missouri, in his book, *Lincoln the Hoosier,* quoted John E. Iglehart of Evansville, Indiana, as saying that he remembered his mother reciting a poem with the same words as the supposed Lincoln song. His mother, who was about nine years old at the time of the Grigsby-Lincoln wedding, had come with her family from England to Saundersville, Indiana, when five years of age. He says that she knew and often recited old English nursery rhymes and the poems of Campbell, Moore, and Burns. Among other poems she had learned, he said, the poem which Mrs. Crawford remembered as the lyrics for Abe's song. Mr. Iglehart says that his mother had memorized these things in her youth. It must be apparent that she learned the one under discussion in her youth in Indiana, not in England, as she left England when five years of age. Nursery rhymes she probably did learn in the Old Country, but it does seem unlikely that as a child of five she would be taught a poem like this. If she learned it after coming to Indiana, there is no proof that she did not acquire it after young Lincoln had sung it and it had gained some currency in the state by oral transmission.

One thing is certain. The idea itself was not original with Lincoln. Following the exhaustive research by Professor Francis Lee Utley, of Ohio State University, and Dr. George Pullen Jackson, Nashville, Tennessee, we can trace the basic idea for the song all the way back to the twelfth century and it is firmly established in "The Parson's Tale" in Chaucer's *Canterbury Tales.* It was reduced to song form and was in print in England as early as 1740. It must be noted, however, that while the idea of the relation between the sexes in the married state, based on the woman's being taken from man's body, is set forth in the same logical manner, the words to the song are not the same as those of any variant found in America. I have found no American version in print earlier than 1844, when it appeared under the title "Creation" in *The Sacred Harp,* compiled by B. F. White and E. J. King. In the 1868 edition of the same compilation, its authorship is attributed to Elder E. Dumas. Under the title "Wedlock" it appears in *The Social Harp,* dated 1854 and credited to Henry F. Chandler. It seems very probable that both of these claimants had picked up the words to the song from oral tradition and, after making certain changes, set them to tunes of their own composing.

Until now there has been nothing offered in evidence to dispute the assumption that these printed versions might have been the outgrowth of the original by young Abe Lincoln, but herewith is presented for the first time evidence that this song in a form very closely approximating Lincoln's version was known in the vicinity of Lincoln's birthplace before the Lincolns moved to Indiana. Mrs. M. Wash Tucker, of Campbellsville, Kentucky, has an old handwritten copy of a song which family traditions say was sung at the wedding of her mother's parents, Rhoda Stiles and Griffin Willett, by a sister of the bride, Mrs. Eunice Stiles Maxwell. This wedding occurred on February 14, 1818, on Rolling Fork River, near Hodgenville, Kentucky, not far from Lincoln's boyhood home. The words of this song, which does not have a title, are very close to the ones Mrs. Crawford says young Lincoln sang and called "Adam and Eve's Wedding." Mrs. Tucker says it is her understanding, from what she has heard older folks say, that this song occupied the same position in connection with marriages of that day that "O Promise Me" has had in our own time.

Of all the versions examined, however, none are exactly like that attributed to Lincoln. In the case of all printed versions, I have seen no two tunes to which these words were sung that are alike. It seems fairly certain that Abe changed some of the lines to suit himself and probably remade the tune to bring it closer to his own vocal abilities. Abraham Lincoln, as much as any other one claimant, is entitled to whatever credit is due the author of "Adam and Eve's Wedding Song." Certainly the title and the word changes are his and the tune to which his words are set is different from any other melody noted down for it.

ADAM AND EVE'S WEDDING SONG

(As remembered by Mrs. Elizabeth Crawford)

When Adam was created, he dwelt in Eden's shade,
As Moses has recorded and soon an Eve was made.
Ten thousand times ten thousand of creatures swarmed around
Before a bride was formed and yet no mate was found.

The Lord then was not willing the man should be alone
But caused a sleep upon him and took from him a bone,
And closed the flesh in that place and then he took the same
And of it made a woman and brought her to the man.

Then Adam he rejoiced to see his loving bride,
A part of his own body, the product of his side.
This woman was not taken from Adam's feet we see,
So he must not abuse her, the meaning seems to be.

This woman was not taken from Adam's head, we know,
To show she must not rule him; 'tis evidently so.
This woman she was taken from under Adam's arm,
So she must be protected from injuries and harm.

Mrs. Crawford mentions one other song that was a favorite with Abe when he was employed as a field hand by her husband. She gives it the title of "John Anderson's Lamentation," and says it was generally believed that Abe had something to do with writing it also, saying, "I know that he was in the habit of making songs and singing of them."

A somewhat similar song appears in *The Social Harp,* with the compiler, John G. McCurry, claiming it in 1851, under the title "John Adkin's Farewell." I have found no other early printing of it and certainly Abe sang it long before that date.

The wonder of it is that Abe, with his sly sense of humor, did not change the last line a bit. After reading of all his self-confessed weaknesses and criminal instincts it would seem that Abe might have been tempted to substitute in Brother Anderson's last line the word "from" for "and."

JOHN ANDERSON'S LAMENTATION

(As remembered by Mrs. Elizabeth Crawford)

O sinners! Poor sinners! Take warning by me;
The fruits of transgression, behold now and see;
My soul is tormented, my body confined;
My friends and dear children left weeping behind.

Much intoxication my ruin has been,
And my dear companion has barbarously slain.
In yonder cold graveyard her body doth lie,
Whilst I am condemned and shortly must die.

Remember John Anderson's death and reform
Before Death overtakes you and vengeance comes on.
My grief's overwhelming, in God I must trust;
I'm justly condemned, my sentence is just.

I am waiting the summons in eternity to be hurled,
Whilst my poor little orphans are cast on the world,
I hope my kind neighbors their guardians will be;
And Heaven, kind Heaven, protect them and me.

During court week in Decatur, Illinois, in 1849, Mrs. Jane Martin Johns arrived to take up temporary residence in the Macon House, favorite stopping place of the legal fraternity while traveling the Eighth Judicial District Circuit. It happened that many of the lawyers were present there when Mrs. Johns's piano arrived by freight wagon. A piano was so much of a novelty that a crowd soon gathered around the wagon to look it over.

Mrs. Johns remembered that when it came to the point of unloading the piano and carrying it into the hotel a tall, dark, friendly man immediately assumed leadership and called on his companions and the bystanders to lend a hand. It was Lincoln, of course, who could hardly wait to hear the piano played; his helpers in the moving job were associates of the bar. They begged her to favor them with some music that night after supper and were all there when she sat down to play.

First, to show them that she was really an accomplished musician, she played the more difficult selections, such as "The Battle of Prague" and "Carnival of Venice." Then she drifted into more popular tunes, like "Washington's March," "Come, Haste to the Wedding" and "Wood Up Quick Step." She next showed her vocal abilities in "The Ship on Fire," "The Lament of the Irish Emigrant," with "Widdy McGee" and "I Wont Be a Nun" in more humorous vein, plus minstrel numbers including "Old Dan Tucker," "Lucy Long," and "Jim Crow." Lincoln and the others joined in on the chorus of these, but dropped out as the going got tough, until only Leonard Swett and a Mr. Brown remained to sing with her "Moonlight Music, Love and Flowers," "Rocked in the Cradle of the Deep," "Pilgrim Fathers," "Bonaparte's Grave" and "Kathleen Mavourneen." When Mrs. Johns herself sang "He Doeth All Things Well," Mr. Lincoln said, "Don't let us spoil that song with any more music tonight." He thanked her for himself and his friends and the party broke up. She says that she later played this favorite song for him many times, at his request.

Mrs. Johns described Abraham Lincoln in 1849 as being a polished gentleman, observing the usual niceties in his association with the opposite sex. She stated that he was well dressed, and commented particularly on his shawl as being rich in texture and fashionable in color. This was Lincoln the successful attorney, who had come a long way from his backwoods ways and manner of dress.

It is hardly necessary to include here all the songs sung by Mrs. Johns for Lincoln and his friends. However, since her program did include many of his known favorites, we have picked these for inclusion, beginning with the highlight of that evening, "He Doeth All Things Well," which is given on the next two pages as it appeared in the edition then in publication.

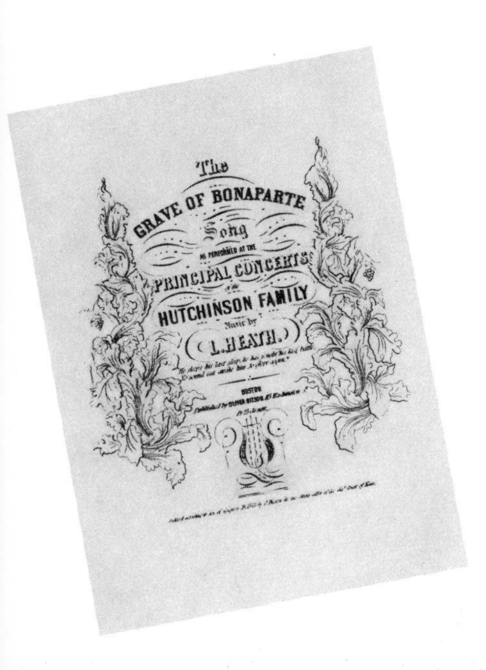

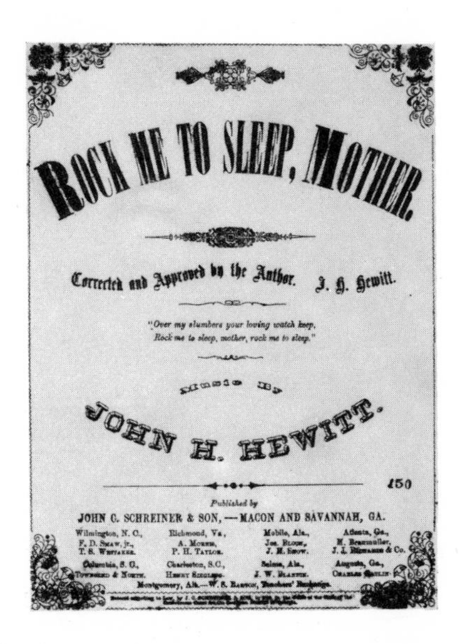

HE DOETH ALL THINGS WELL.

3

Years fled — that little sister then was dear as *life* to me
And woke, in my unconscious heart, a wild idolatry,
I worshipped at an earthly shrine, lured by some magic spell,
Forgetful of the praise of Him "who doeth all things well."

4

She was the lovely star, whose light around my pathway shone,
Amid this darksome vale of tears, through which I journey on,
Its radiance had obscured the light, which round His throne doth dwell,
And I wandered far away from Him, "who doeth all things well."

5

That star went down in beauty — yet it shineth sweetly now,
In the bright and dazzling coronet, that decks the Savior's brow,
She bowed to the Destroyer — whose shafts none may repel,
But we know, for God hath told us, "He doeth all things well."

6

I remember well my sorrow, as I stood beside her bed,
And my deep and heartfelt anguish, when they told me *she was dead;*
And oh! that cup of bitterness — *let not my heart rebel,*
God gave — He took — He will restore — "He doeth all things well."

It is known that Lincoln was very fond of "The Lament of The Irish Emigrant," reproduced here from an early sheet-music copy. It was a popular song of its period and ran to several editions. He especially liked the verse beginning, "I'm very lonely now, Mary."

I'm very lonely now, Mary,
For the poor make no new friends,
But oh! they love the better far,
The few our Father sends!
And you were all I had, Mary,
My blessing and my pride;
There's nothing left to care for now,
Since my poor Mary died.

Yours was the brave good heart, Mary,
That still kept hoping on,
When the trust in God had left my soul,
And my arm's young strength had gone;
There was comfort ever on your lip,
And the kind look on your brow;
I bless you for that same, Mary,
Though you can't hear me now.

I thank you for that patient smile,
When your heart was fit to break,
When the hunger pain was gnawing there,
And you hid it, for my sake,
I bless you for the pleasant word,
When your heart was sad and sore;
Oh, I'm thankful you are gone, Mary,
Where grief can't reach you more.

I'm bidding you a long farewell,
My Mary, kind and true,
But I'll not forget you, darling,
In the land I'm going to,
They say there's bread and work for all,
And the sun shines always there;
But I'll not forget old Ireland,
Were it fifty times as fair.

And often in those grand old woods,
I'll sit and shut my eyes,
And my heart will travel back again,
To the place where Mary lies,
And I'll think I see the little stile,
Where we sat side by side;
And the springing corn, and the bright May morn,
When first you were my bride.

"I Wont Be A Nun" apparently was not widely known in sheet-music form at the time of Mrs. Johns's concert, as I have been unable to find a copy of that date. It is given here as found in my copy of Grigg's *Southern and Western Songster,* published in Philadelphia in 1829. The tune used is the one to which I have heard it sung in years past.

I WONT BE A NUN

Now is it not a pity such a pretty girl as I
Should be sent to a nunnery to pine away and die?
But I wont be a nun — no, I wont be a nun;
I'm so fond of pleasure that I cannot be a nun.

I'm sure I cannot tell what's the mischief I have done,
But my mother oft tells me that I must be a nun.
But I wont be a nun — no, I wont be a nun;
I'm so fond of pleasure that I cannot be a nun.

I could not bear confinement, it would not do for me,
For I like to go a-shopping, and to see what I can see.
So I wont be a nun — no, I wont be a nun;
I'm so fond of pleasure that I cannot be a nun.

I love to hear men flattering — love fashionable clothes,
I love music and dancing and chatting with the beaux.
So I cant be a nun — no, I wont be a nun;
I'm so fond of pleasure that I cannot be a nun.

So, mother, don't be angry now, but let your daughter be,
For the nuns would not like to have a novice wild as me.
And I cant be a nun — no, I wont be a nun;
I'm so fond of pleasure that I cannot be a nun.

"Come, Haste to the Wedding" has long been a popular number with old-time fiddlers. The claim has been made for it that it was one of the favorites of President George Washington. It is printed here as it appears in an old book of fiddle tunes in the Renfro Valley collection, often used on radio programs originating from Renfro Valley Settlement in the Kentucky hill country.

COME, HASTE TO THE WEDDING

"The Wood Up Quick Step" played by Mrs. Johns for Lincoln and his friends is included here because it was a popular piece of music of its time that is now rarely seen, whereas "The Battle of Prague" and "Carnival of Venice" are often found, as is "Washington's March."

1st time.
2d time.
Post Horn.
Trumpet.
Bugle.
Post Horn.
Bugle.

KATHLEEN

MAVOURNEEN.

Composed by F. W. N. CROUCH.

Kathleen Mavourneen, awake from thy slumbers,
The blue mountains glow in the sun's golden light,
Ah! where is the spell that once hung on my slumbers,
Arise in thy beauty, thou star of my night,
Arise in thy beauty, thou star of my night.
Mavourneen, Mavourneen, my sad tears are falling,
To think that from Erin and thee I must part,
It may be for years, and it may be forever,
Then why art thou silent, thou voice of my heart?
It may be for years, and it may be forever,
Then why art thou silent, Kathleen Mavourneen?

THE GRAVE OF BONAPARTE.

2

Oh, shade of the mighty, where now are the legions
That rush'd but to conquer when thou ledst them on;
Alas! they have perished in far hilly regions,
And all save the fame of their triumph is gone.
The trumpet may sound, and the loud cannon rattle,
They heed not, they hear not, they're free from all pain;
They sleep their last sleep, they have fought their last battle,
No sound can awake them to glory again,
No sound can awake them to glory again.

3

Yet, spirit immortal, the tomb cannot bind thee,
For, like thine own eagle that soared to the sun,
Thou springest from bondage, and leavest behind thee
A name, which before thee no mortal had won.
Though nations may combat, and war's thunders rattle,
No more on the steed wilt thou sweep o'er the plain;
Thou sleep'st thy last sleep, thou hast fought thy last battle.
No sound can awake thee to glory again!
No sound can awake thee to glory again!

Lincoln was a lifelong admirer of the Negro minstrel songs so much in vogue in his day. Nothing could more quickly arouse him from a fit of despondency than a rollicking nonsense song of this type. Ward Hill Lamon, his close friend and associate through the years, said Lincoln's favorite was "De Blue-Tailed Fly," which Lincoln called "that buzzing song." In its earlier printings it was often entitled "Jim Crack Corn." Lincoln also showed a preference for "Lucy Long," "Old Dan Tucker," "Jim Crow," "Jim Along Josey" and "Zip Coon," which the Grigsby boys referred to as "Old Sukey Blue-Skin." Another friend remembered that he liked "Miss Flora McFlimsey," listing it among his favorite minstrel songs, but I have never been able to find a song of that name.

"Nothing to Wear" he liked, a somewhat lengthy humorous recitation about Miss Flora McFlimsey, but it is doubtful if it was ever reduced to the limits of a song.

Lincoln was almost childish in his enjoyment of a minstrel show. He would neglect business or pass up a chance at almost any other type of entertainment to attend a minstrel performance. Henry C. Whitney told of being in Chicago with Lincoln in the latter part of 1860, only a few months before his nomination as a candidate for the presidency, and taking him to see the Rumsey and Newcomb Minstrels. The occasion was made memorable to Lincoln by his hearing that night, for the first time, the new song "Dixie's Land." Whitney said he was so pleased with it that he applauded louder and longer than anyone else and called out, over and over, "Let's have it again! Let's have it again!"

Although published in the North and credited to a Northern minstrel and song-writer, Daniel Decatur Emmett, "Dixie's Land" became so popular in the South that soon after the beginning of the War Between the States it became generally recognized as the rallying song of the Southern Confederacy. There might have been more justification for this strange affinity than we know. Family and friends of Will S. Hays, author-composer, of Louisville, Kentucky, have maintained that Hays originated the melody, to be used as a marching song in a parade held in Louisville during a time when Emmett was appearing at a local theater and had an opportunity to pick up the catchy tune, remember it, and later appropriate it. Since Hays had not bothered to have the tune published or copyrighted, there is, of course, no way to know whether or not he is entitled to the credit claimed for him.

Lincoln always included "Dixie" among his favorites. A few days after the close of the war he astonished everyone by calling for it when he was being serenaded by a military band. When he said, "It's our tune now," I do not believe, as many embittered Southerners — my great-grandmother Matilda Dalton Coffey among them — believed, that he meant to say that "Dixie" belonged to the North by right of conquest; I believe he meant that here on the common ground of admiration for a good song the North and the South could find a unity, a fellowship, of enjoyment and appreciation.

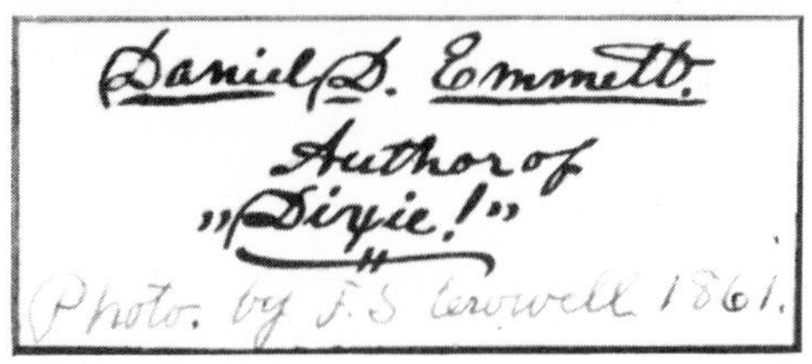

"Dixie's Land" is reproduced from an original copy by its "author and composer," Daniel Decatur Emmett, now in the possession of Mr. Ogden Wintermute, of Emmett's home town, Mt. Vernon, Ohio.

2 — Old missus marry Will D' Weaber,
Will he was a gay deceaber;
When he put his arm around 'er,
He look fierce like a 40 pound 'er.
Chorus. Den I wish I was. etc.

3 — His face was sharp like a butchers cleaber,
But dat did not seem to greab 'er;
How could she act de foolish part,
An marry a man to broke her heart.
Chorus. Den I wish I was. etc

4 — Buckwheat cakes an stony batter,
Makes you fat or a little fatter;
Here's a health to de next old missus,
An all de galls dat want to kiss us.
Chorus. Den I wish I was, etc

5 — Now if you want to drive 'way sorrow,
Come an hear dis song tomorrow;
Den hoe it down an scratch yoa grabble,
To Dixie's Land I'm bound to trabble.
Chorus. Den I wish I was, etc.

Mr. T. RICE
AS
THE ORIGINAL JIM CROW
N. 29 Chatham St.
JIM ALONG JOSEY.
As Sung by,
Mr. JOHN N. SMITH.
Arranged for the
PIANO FORTE.
BY
AN EMINENT PROFESSOR.

ZIP COON.
A favorite Comic Song.

JIM ALONG JOSEY

6

I'm de nigger that don't mind my troubles,
Because dey are noting more dan bubbles,
De ambition that dis nigger feels
Is showing de science of his heels.
Hey get along, get along Josey,
Hey get along, Jim along Joe!

7

De fust President we eber had was Gen'ral Washington,
And de one we got now is Martin Van Buren,
But altho' Gen'ral Washington's dead
As long as de country stands his name shall float ahead.
Hey get along, get along Josey,
Hey get along, Jim along Joe!

2

Oh! when I gets dat new coat which I expects to hab soon,
Likewise a new pair tight-kneed trousaloon,
Den I walks up and down Broadway wid my Susanna,
And de white folks will take me to be Santa Anna.
Hey get along, get along Josey,
Hey get along, Jim along Joe!

3

My sister Rose de oder night did dream,
Dat she was floating up and down de stream,
And when she woke she begon to cry,
And de white cat picked out de black cat's eye.
Hey get along, get along Josey,
Hey get along, Jim along Joe!

4

Now way down south not very far off,
A bullfrog died wid de whooping cough,
And do oder side of Mississippi as you must know,
Dare's where I was christen'd Jim along Joe.
Hey get along, get along Josey,
Hey get along, Jim along Joe!

5

De New York niggers tink dey're fine,
Because dey drink de genuine,
De southern niggers dey lib on mush,
And when dey laugh dey say *Oh Hush.*
Hey get along, get along Josey,
Hey get along, Jim along Joe!

II

Oh I'm a roarer on de Fiddle,
And down in old Virginny,
They say I play de skyentific
Like Massa Pagannini.

III

I went down to de riber,
I didn't mean to stay,
But dere I see so many gals,
I couldn't get away.

IV

I git 'pon a flat boat,
I catch de Uncle Sam,
Den I went to see de place
Wher dey kill'd Packen-
ham.

V

An den I go to Orleans
An feel so full of fight
Dey put me in de Calaboose,
An keep me dere all night.

VIII

I sit upon a Hornet's nest,
I dance upon my head,
I tie a Wiper round my neck
And den I goes to bed.

IX

Dere's Possum up de gumtree,
An Raccoon in de hollow,
Wake Snakes for June bugs
Stole my half a dollar.

VI

When I got out I hit a man,
His name I now forget,
But dere was nothing left
'Cept a little grease spot.

VII

I wip my weight in wildcats
I eat an Alligator,
And tear up more ground
Dan kiver 50 load of tater.

X

A ring-tail'd monkey,
An a rib-nose Baboon,
Went out de odder day
To spend de arternoon.

XI

Oh de way dey bake de hoe
cake
In old Virginny neber tire,
Dey put de dough upon de
foot,
An hole it to de fire.

XII

Oh by trade I am a carpenter,
But be it understood,
De way I get my liben is,
By sawing de tick oh wood.

XIII

I'm a full blooded niggar,
Ob de real ole stock,
An wid my head and shoulder
I can split a horse block.

XIV

I'm so glad dat I'm a niggar,
An don't you wish you was too,
For den you'd gain popularity,
By jumping Jim Crow.

XV

Now my brodder niggars,
I do not think it right,
Dat you should laugh at dem
Who happen to be white.

XVI

Kase it dar misfortune,
An dey'd spend ebery dollar,
If dey only could be,
Gentlemen ob color.

XVII

It almost break my heart,
To see dem envy me,
An from my soul I wish dem,
Full as black as we.

XVIII

What stuff it is in dem,
To make de Debbil black
I'll prove dat he is white,
In de twinkling of a crack.

XIX

For you see, loved brodders,
As true as he hab a tail,
It is his berry wickedness,
What makes him turn pale.

XX

I went to Hoboken,
To hab a promenade,
An dar I see de pretty gals,
Drinking de lemonade.

XXI

Dat sour and dat sweet,
Is berry good by gum,
But de best of lemonade is,
Made by adding rum.

PICAYUNE BUTLER

Away down souf whar I was born,
I worked all day in de fields of corn.
Yah, yah, yah!
When de sun shines hot de niggars roast
And when dey dance dey sweat de most,
Yah, yah, yah!

Ob all de gals I ebber see
Miss Lucy Neal was best to me,
Yah, yah, yah!
She chased de bulgine out of breff
And dat's what caused Miss Lucy's deff,
Yah, yah, yah!

Here I am a-gwine to sing
An gwine to mek de banjo ring.
Yah, yah, yah!
Dis song I know'l please you to deff
And laugh you nearly out of breff,
Yah, yah, yah!

CHORUS:
Picayune Butler, coming, coming,
Picayune Butler come to town.
Ahoo, ahoo, ahoo, ahoo, ahoo, ahoo!
Picayune Butler, coming, coming,
Picayune Butler come to town.

NEW YORK *Published at* MILLETS MUSIC SALOON *329 Broadway.*

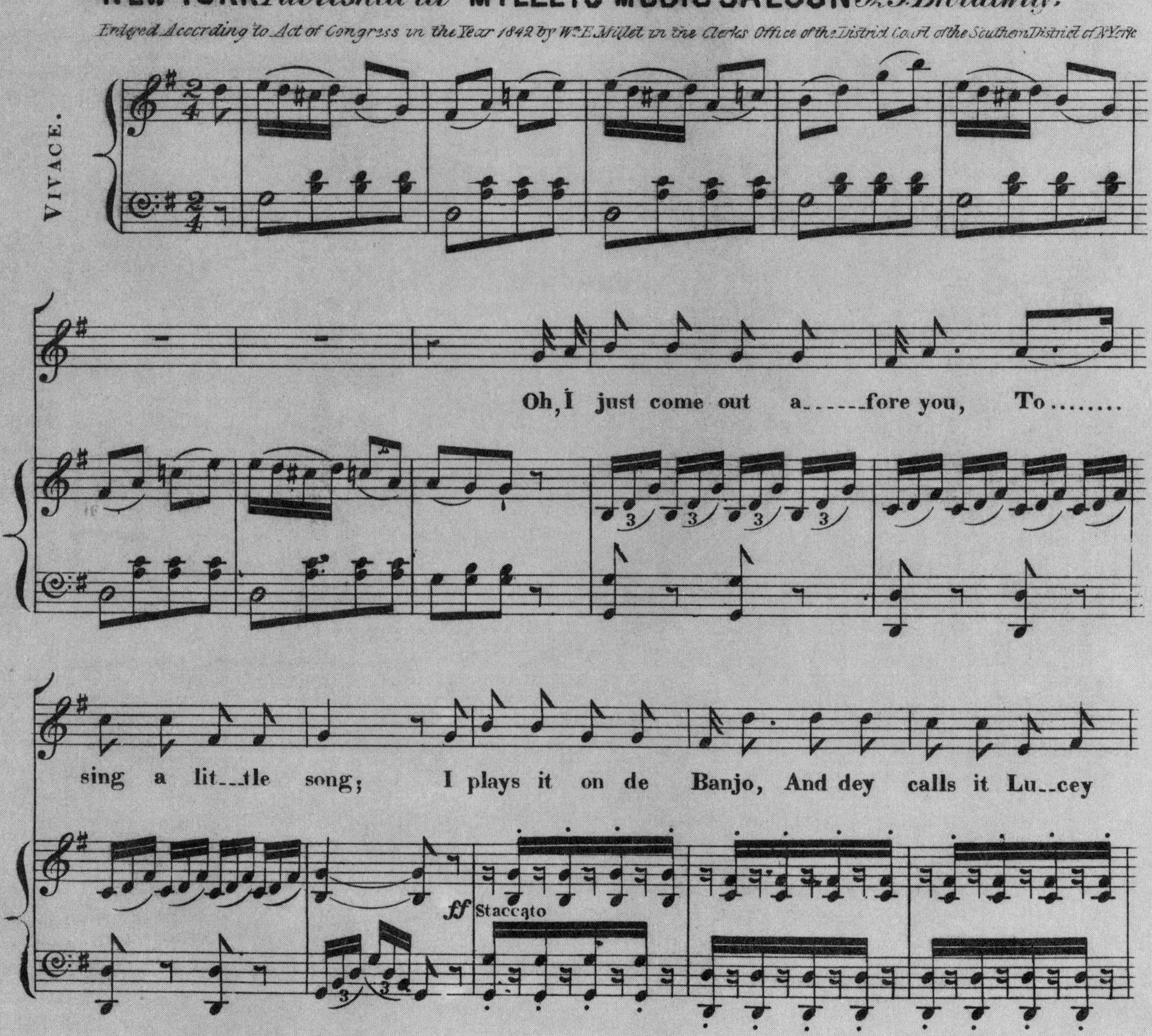

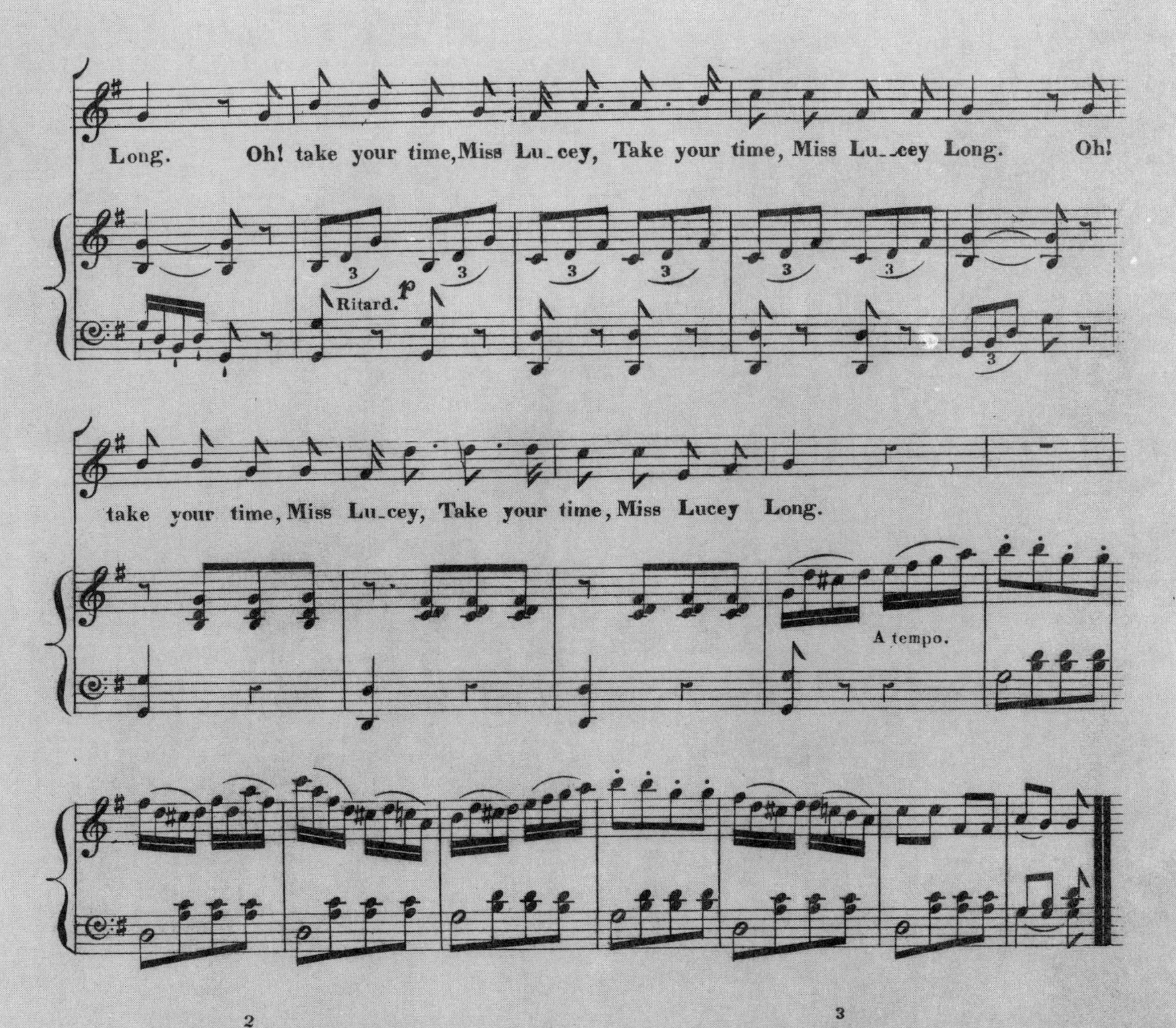

2

Miss Lucey, she is handsome,
And Miss Lucey, she is tall;
To see her dance Cachucha,
Is death to Niggers all.
Oh! take your time, &c.

3

Oh! Miss Lucey's teeth is grinning,
Just like an ear ob corn,
And her eyes dey look so winning—
Oh! would I'd ne'er been born.
Oh! take your time, &c.

4

I axed her for to marry
Myself de toder day,
She said she'd rather tarry,
So I let her habe her way.
Oh! take your time, &c.

5

If she makes a scolding wife,
As sure as she was born,
I'll tote her down to Georgia,
And trade her off for corn.
Oh! take your time, &c.

6

My Mamma's got de tisic,
And my Daddy's got de gout:
Good morning, Mister Phisick!
Does your mother know you'r out
Oh! take your time, &c.

THE VIRGINIA MINSTRELS,
Nº 5
"JIM CRACK CORN"
or the Blue tail Fly,
Composed for the
PIANO FORTE.

Published by F. D BENTEEN Baltimore.

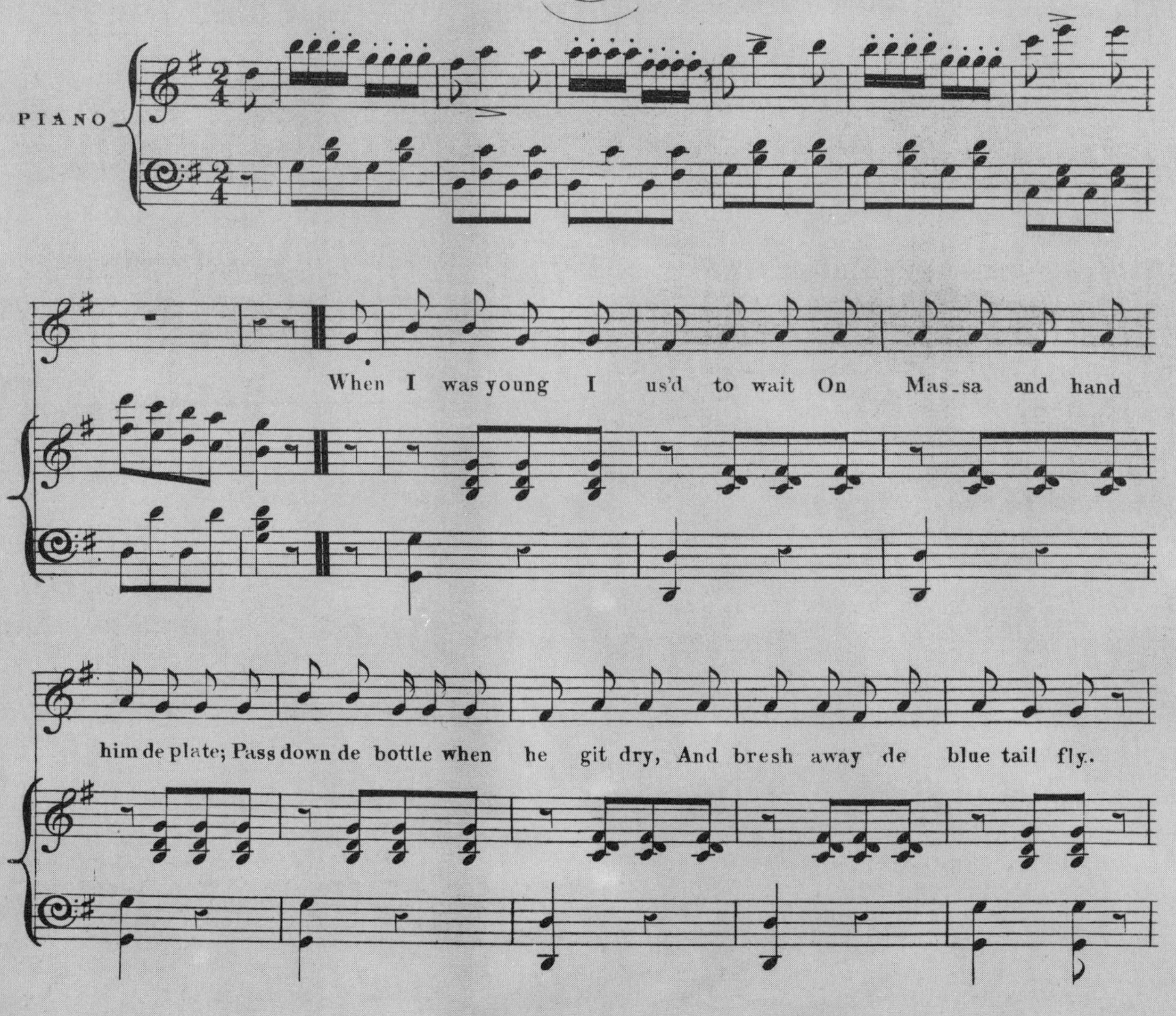
PIANO
When I was young I us'd to wait On Mas_sa and hand
him de plate; Pass down de bottle when he git dry, And bresh away de blue tail fly.

2.
Den arter dinner massa sleep,
He bid dis niggar vigil keep;
An' when he gwine to shut his eye,
He tell me watch de blue tail fly.
Jim crack corn &c.

3.
An' when he ride in de arternoon,
I foller wid a hickory broom;
De poney being berry shy,
When bitten by de blue tail fly.
Jim crack corn &c.

4.
One day he rode aroun' de farm,
De flies so numerous dey did swarm;
One chance to bite 'im on the thigh,
De debble take dat blu tail fly.
Jim crack corn &c.

5.
De poney run, he jump an' pitch,
An' tumble massa in de ditch;
He died, an' de jury wonder'd why
De verdic was de blue tail fly.
Jim crack corn &c.

6.
Dey laid 'im under a 'simmon tree,
His epitaph am dar to see:
'Beneath dis stone I'm forced to lie,
All by de means ob de blue tail fly.
Jim crack corn &c.

7.
Ole massa gone, now let 'im rest,
Dey say all tings am for de best;
I nebber forget till de day I die,
Ole massa an' dat blue tail fly.
Jim crack corn &c.

ZIP COON
A FAVORITE COMIC SONG
Sung by
MR. G.W. DIXON.
VOICE.
ALLEGRO MAESTOSO.
PIANO
FORTE.
f
O ole Zip Coon he is a larned skoler, O
ole Zip Coon he is a larned skolar, O ole Zip Coon he is a larned skolar, Sings

2

O its old Suky blue skin, she is in lub wid me
I went the udder arter noon to take a dish ob tea;
What do you tink now, Suky hab for supper,
Why chicken foot an possum heel, widout any butter.

3

Did you eber see the wild goose, sailing on de ocean,
O de wild goos motion is a berry pretty notion;
Ebry time de wild goos, beckens to de swaller,
You hear him google google google google gollar.

4

I went down to Sandy Hollar tother arternoon
And the first man I chanc'd to meet war ole Zip Coon;
Ole Zip Coon he is a natty scholar,
For he plays upon de Banjo "Cooney in de hollar."

5

My old Missus she's mad wid me,
Kase I would'nt go wid her into Tennessee,
Massa build him barn and put in de fodder
Twas dis ting and dat ting one ting or odder.

6

I pose you heard ob de battle New Orleans,
Whar ole Gineral Jackson gib de British beans;
Dare de Yankee boys do de job so slick
For dey cotch old Packenham an row'd him up de creek.

7

I hab many tings to tork about but don't know wich cum first,
So here de tost to old Zip Coon before he gin to rust;
May he hab de pretty girls, like de King ob ole,
To sing dis song so many times, fore he turn to mole.

The Original

OLD DAN TUCKER.

2

Tucker is a nice old man,
He use to ride our darby ram;
He sent him whizzen down de hil
If he had'nt got up he'd lay dar s
Get out, &

3

Here's my razor in good order
Magnum bonum—jis hab bought 'e
Sheep shell oats, Tucker shell de
I'll shabe you soon as de water ge
Get out &

4

Ole Dan Tucker an I got drunk,
He fell in de fire an kick up a ch
De charcoal got inside he shoe
Lor bless you honey how de ashes
Get out &

5

Down de road foremost de stump,
Massa make me work de pump;
I pump so hard I broke de sucker
Dar was work for ole Dan Tucker.
Get out, &

6

I went to town to buy some goods
I lost myself in a piece of woods,
De night was dark I had to suffer,
It froze de heel of Daniel Tucker.
Get out &

7

Tucker was a hardened sinner,
He nebber said his grace at dinner
De ole sow squeel, de pigs did squ
He hole hog wid de tail and all.
Get out, &

One of the family theatrical groups touring the country in the late forties was the Newhall Family, of Jackson, Illinois. The troupe consisted of the father, mother, brother, two sisters, and a young man by the name of Hillis, who later became the husband of one of the sisters, Lois E. Newhall.

It happened that their itinerary often crossed or coincided with that of the members of the legal fraternity traveling the Illinois Eighth Judicial Circuit. Lincoln and Miss Newhall showed such an interest in each other and such a fondness for each other's company that his fellow attorneys joked him incessantly about it at first, but later began to take a more serious view of it, reminding Lincoln that he was a married man and held a responsible position in life. He assured them that their alarm was entirely uncalled for, that he felt no more than a friendly interest in Miss Newhall who, he said, was the only woman except his wife who ever bothered to pay him a compliment.

Many years later Miss Newhall, then Mrs. Hillis, told one of her music pupils of this friendship with the man who had risen to the highest position in the land. She said that in 1849, when she was sixteen years old, their family troupe for several days traveled the same circuit as the circuit court did. They stopped at the same hotels in the various towns visited and it was customary for the family and members of the bar to assemble in the lobby or sitting room of the hotel after the performance each evening, at which time she and her sisters would sing for them until well along in the evening.

She recalled that, on the last night they were to be together before her troupe branched off on another route, they sang and played until a late hour, the hotel being one of the few that boasted a melodeon for the use and pleasure of its guests. One of the lawyers present turned to Lincoln and in a very serious tone asked him if he did not think it was time for him to sing for the young ladies who had entertained them so long and so well. Lincoln, of course, made immediate denial of any ability as a singer, but his friends would not let him off so easily, hugely enjoying his embarrassment before Miss Newhall and her sister, to whom they confided that Lincoln was really a very accomplished singer, so much so that back in his home district he was often called on to sing at sales and auctions to help draw a crowd. Realizing what his friends were up to, Lincoln arose and declared he was going up to bed. On his way out of the parlor he had to pass by the melodeon where Miss Newhall was seated. She stopped him to say that if he had a song he would like to sing she felt sure that she could accompany him on the melodeon, even if she had never heard the song before. She later quoted him as saying, "Why, Miss Newhall, if it was to save my soul I couldn't imitate a note that you could touch on that. I never sang in my life and was never able to. Those fellows are just simply liars, but I'll tell you what I'll do for you. Since you girls have been so kind singing for us I'll repeat to you my favorite poem." Then leaning easily against the door frame he recited his favorite verses, beginning "Oh! why should the spirit of mortal be proud?" When she expressed an interest in the poem he promised to copy it off for her that night after going to his room.

It was understood that the court group planned on leaving very early next morning. Miss Newhall was eating breakfast by herself, by candlelight, when Lincoln came into the dining room. She remembers that she was eating pancakes and was in the act of cutting one up when she sensed his presence behind her. Then, as she recalls, "a great big hand took hold of my left hand, or rather covering it on the table, and with his right hand around over my other shoulder he laid down a piece of paper just in front of my plate. Before I could realize who or what it was, Mr. Lincoln moved toward the door saying, 'Goodbye, my dear!' That was the last time I ever saw him."

Henry Clay Whitney, however, said that in 1855 he was attending court in Bloomington in company with Lincoln. He said that Lincoln went alone to a concert being given there by the Newhall family. Lois was then Mrs. Hillis. If, as she said years later, she never saw him again after 1849, perhaps he did not make his presence known at this and other times when he was in the audience at their concerts. One of the numbers she is said to have sung for him was "Ben Bolt."

2

Oh! don't you remember the wood, Ben Bolt,
Near the green sunny slope of the hill;
Where oft we have sung 'neath its wide-spreading shade,
And kept time to the click of the mill.
The mill has gone to decay, Ben Bolt,
And a quiet now reigns all around,
See the old rustic porch, with its roses so sweet,
Lies scatter'd and fallen to the ground.
See the old rustic porch, with its roses so sweet,
Lies scatter'd and fallen to the ground.

3

Oh! don't you remember the school, Ben Bolt,
And the Master so kind and so true,
And the little nook by the clear-running brook,
Where we gather'd the flow'rs as they grew.
On the Master's grave grows the grass, Ben Bolt,
And the running little brook is now dry;
And of all the friends who were schoolmates then,
There remains, Ben, but you and I.
And of all the friends who were schoolmates then,
There remains, Ben, but you and I.

The poem beginning "Oh! why should the spirit of mortal be proud?" was the one Lincoln recited for Miss Newhall and later copied off for her. It was generally known as his favorite. So closely did it become linked with him that a piece of sheet music published after his death credits the words to him, which was, of course, incorrect. It has been assumed that Lincoln wrote, or at least made changes in, other songs, but so far as I can find this is the only instance in which his name appears on any song as the author of the words.

OH, WHY SHOULD THE SPIRIT OF MORTAL BE PROUD?

dim.
slow.
break of the wave, He passeth from life to his rest in the grave! The leaves of the
oak and the willow shall fade, Be scatter'd a - round and to - gether be laid; And the
with great feeling.
young and the old, and the low and the high, Shall crumble to dust, and to gether shall lie.
CHORUS.
Air.
'Tis the wink of an eye, 'tis the draught of a breath, From the
Alto.
Tenor.
'Tis the wink of an eye, 'tis the draught of a breath, From the
Bass.
ACCOMP'T.
f
pp

blos - som of health, to the paleness of death, From the gild - ed sa - loon, to the
blos - som of health, to the paleness of death; From the gild - ed sa - loon, to the

rall
bier and the shroud! Oh! why should the spir - it of mor - tal be proud?
bier and the shroud! Oh! why should the spir - it of mor - tal be proud?

2

The hand of the king that the sceptre hath borne;
The brow of the priest that the mitre hath worn;
The eye of the sage, and the heart of the brave,
Are hidden and lost in the depths of the grave.
The peasant, whose lot was to sow and to reap,
The herdsman, who climbed with his goats up the steep;
The beggar, who wandered in search of his bread
Have faded away like the grass that we tread.

Quartette 'Tis the wink of an eye, &c.

3

For we are the same, our father's have been;
We see the same sights our father's have seen;
We drink the same stream and view the same sun,
And run the same course our father's have run.
The thoughts we are thinking our father's would think;
From the death we are shrinking our father's would shrink;
To the life we are clinging, they also would cling;
But it speeds for us all, like a bird on the wing.

Quartette 'Tis the wink of an eye, &c.

4

They died!— aye! they died; we things that are now,
That walk on the turf that lies over their brow,
And make in their dwellings a transient abode,
Meet the things that *they* met, on *their* pilgrimage road.
Yea! hope and despondency, pleasure and pain,
We mingle together in sunshine and rain
And the smile and the tear— the song and the dirge,
Still follow each other like surge upon surge.
'Tis the wink of an eye, 'tis the draught of a breath,
From the blossom of health, to the paleness of death;
From the gilded saloon, to the bier and the shroud!
Oh! why should the spirit of mortal be proud?

A professional family singing group Mr. Lincoln liked very much was the Hutchinson Family — and well he might, for it was believed that their singing and campaigning for him was a factor in his election to the presidency. One of the family, John Wallace Hutchinson, published in 1860 the *Lincoln and Liberty* Republican songster, with nine of its fifty titles bearing Lincoln's name and most of the remainder about him or the Republican Party.

The original Hutchinson Family made their first professional appearance in 1841 and soon became famous, not only for their vocal accomplishments but also for their ability to write the songs they made popular in their concert tours. In 1851 they sang in a concert at Springfield, Illinois, where Lincoln probably heard them for the first time. He was so much impressed by their performance that ten years later at a White House performance he asked them to repeat a song he had heard them sing in Springfield.

The Hutchinson family were intensely patriotic. They thought it their duty to sing for the entertainment of the Union soldiers around Washington — not only the wounded in the Federal hospitals, but those on active duty in the various encampments. They were able through the intercession of Secretary Chase to secure passes from Secretary of War Cameron and went to Fairfax Seminary chapel, near Alexandria, Virginia, for their first concert. During the program they caused a near-riot by singing John Greenleaf Whittier's "Hymn of Liberty," with its nine verses set to the tune of Martin Luther's "Ein Feste Burg Ist Unser Gott." Apparently even among the Union ranks were men who were not so opposed to slavery as to feel that it was the great evil portrayed by the lyrics of the aroused Whittier. They took noisy exception to such verses from it as:

What gives the wheatfields blades of steel?
What points the Rebel cannon?
What sits the roaring rabble's heel
On the old star-spangled pennon?
What breaks the oath o' the men of the South?
What whets the knife for the Union's life? —
Hark to the answer; Slavery!

Within twenty-four hours after the disturbance caused by the incident, General McClellan had revoked the passes issued to the Hutchinsons and had forbidden their further appearances before the soldiers. Later the song was shown to President Lincoln, who declared he saw nothing wrong with it and gave orders that if various commanders wanted to invite the Hutchinsons to sing for their troops they had permission to do so.

When the family sang at the White House the President said to J. W. Hutchinson, "I remember one song that you sang when you were in Springfield. It was a good while ago — ten years, perhaps — but I never have forgotten it. It was about a ship on fire, and I want to hear it again." For years this song was one of those featured in the Hutchinson family concerts. It was performed so effectively that once in a Pennsylvania city someone hearing it turned in the fire alarm and brought the fire engines to the scene. The rousing key portion of the song is reproduced here from the original sheet music.

then a tramp— and a rout— And an uproar of voi_ces a_
tempo a poco.
p
p
cres
_rose in the air, And the mother knelt down— and a half spo_ken pray'r, That she
ff
of_fer'd to God in her a_ _ _ _ go_ _ny wild Was fa_ _ther have mer_cy look
ff
down, look down on my child: She flew........ to her husband, she clung....... to his
tempo.
fff
staccato.
ff
side, Oh there was her re_ _ _ fuge what e'er might be_ _tide.

f > con forza.
f >
Fire! Fire! it was raging above and below, And the
cheeks of the Sailors grew pale at the sight, And their eyes glist_'ned wild in the glare of the light; 'Twas
vain o'er the ravage the waters to drip, The pitiless flame was the lord of the ship, and the
rinforzando.
smoke, in thick wreaths, mounted higher, and higher, Oh
f
ff
cres
God it is fearful to perish by Fire; A
a tempo.

dim.
poco.
a poco e piano
lone.......... with des_truc_tion, a___lone........ on the sea, Great
ritenuto.
Fa_ther of mer__cy, our hope is in thee.
pp
pp
ppp
tempo di marcia ma a poco ritenuto.
Sad at heart and resign'd, yet un_daunt_ed and brave, They lower'd the boat a mere speck on the wave, First
quieto.
en_ter'd the mother en_fold_ing her child, It knew she ca_ress'd it look'd up_wards and smil'd, Cold
cold was the night as they drifted away, And mis_ti_ly dawn'd o'er the path_way the day, And they
p

pray'd for the light and at noon_tide a_bout, The sun o'er the waters shone joy_ous_ly out, Ho! a
quasi con energia ma a poco.
sail! Ho! a sail! cried the man on the lee, Ho! a sail! and they turn'd their glad eyes o'er the sea, They
a poco agitato e presto.
see us they see us the sig_ _nal is wav'd, They bear down up_on us they bear down up_
con energio.
_on us they bear down up_on us the sig_nal is wav'd, thank
sf
sf
sf
sf
God, thank God, we're sav'd.
p
pp
pp

"ROCK ME TO SLEEP, MOTHER!"

BALLAD.

Words by FLORENCE PERCY. Music by JOHN H. HEWITT.

The Hutchinson Family repertoire included another Lincoln favorite — "Rock Me to Sleep, Mother." He heard them sing it at a soldiers' hospital and again at the White House. Knowing his worshipful attitude toward his mother and the many disappointments life had brought him, it is easy to understand how this song must have impressed him. He is supposed to have presented to the Hutchinsons during their White House visit the brass thimble which his mother had once owned. I can think of none of their songs which might have been more responsible for this action.

This poem by Elizabeth Akers ("Florence Percy") was set to music by different composers. There is reason for believing that this is the version which the President most admired.

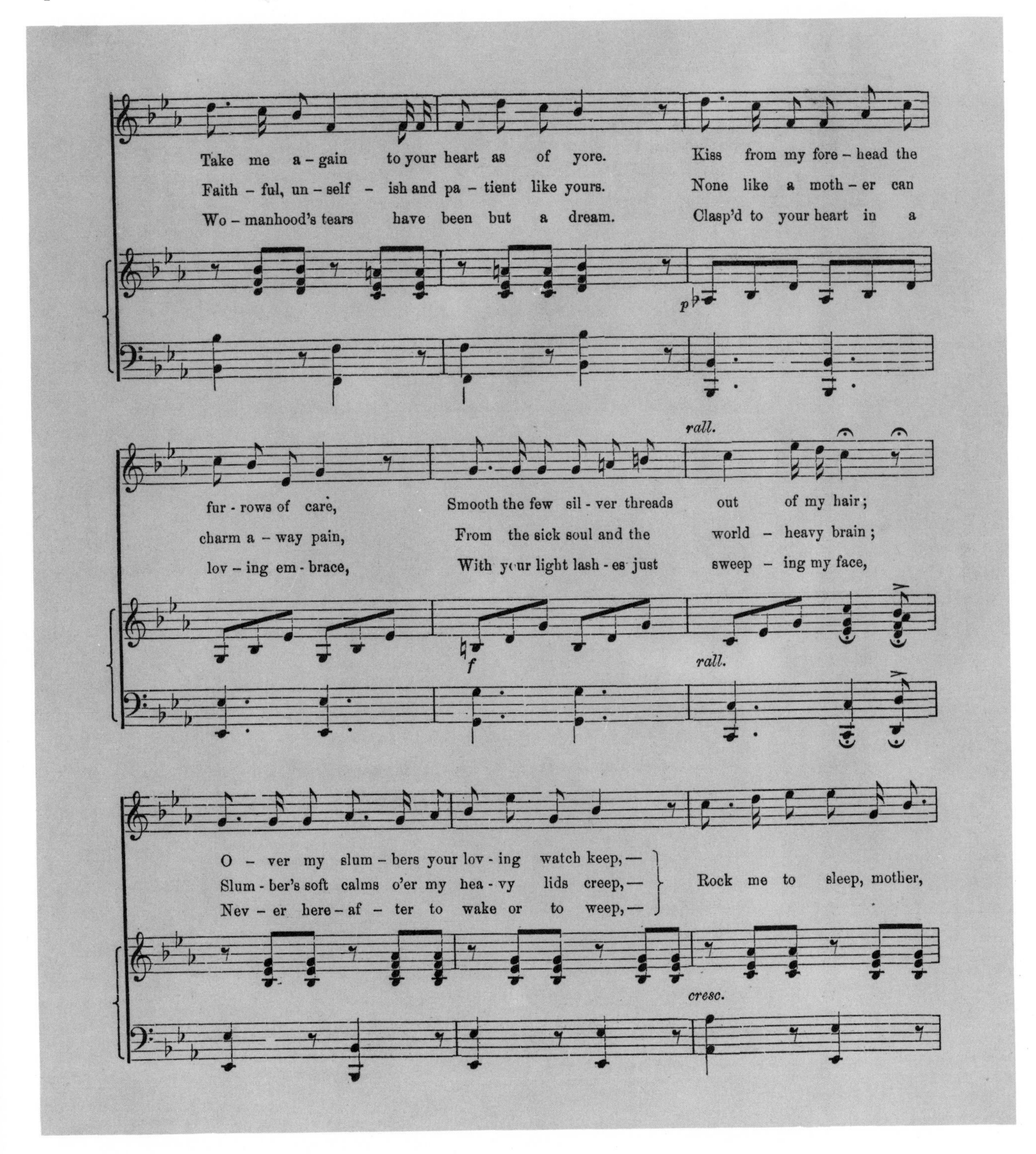

In the presidential election of 1864 General McClellan was the Democratic nominee opposing Lincoln. It was only natural that the opposition press would drag out everything available to lower the President in the eyes of the voters. One thing the *New York World* delighted in retelling was an incident supposed to have happened two years before, immediately following the Battle of Antietam. In an article captioned "One of Mr. Lincoln's Little Jokes" it said, in part: "The second verse of our campaign song published on this page was probably suggested by an incident which occurred on the battlefield of Antietam a few days after the fight. While the President was driving over the field in an ambulance, accompanied by Marshal Lamon, General McClellan and another officer, heavy details of men were engaged in the task of burying the dead. The ambulance had just reached the neighborhood of the old stone bridge, where the dead were piled highest, when Mr. Lincoln, suddenly slapping Marshal Lamon on the knee, exclaimed, 'Come, Lamon, give us the song about Picayune Butler; McClellan has never heard it.' 'Not now, if you please,' said General McClellan with a shudder: 'I would prefer to hear it some other place and time.' "

The verse of the campaign song referred to evidently went like this:

The President has known me intimately for nearly twenty years, and has often heard me sing little ditties. The battle of Antietam was fought on the 17th day of September 1862. On the first day of October, just two weeks after the battle, the President, with some others, including myself, started from Washington to visit the Army, reaching Harper's Ferry at noon of that day. In a short while Gen. McClellan came from his Head Quarters near the battle ground, joined the President, and with him, reviewed the troops at Bolivar Heights that afternoon; and, at night, returned to his Head Quarters, leaving the President at Harper's Ferry. On the morning of the second the President, with Gen. Sumner, reviewed the troops respectively at Loudon Heights and Maryland Heights, and at about noon, started to Gen. McClellan's Head Quarters, reaching there only in time to see very little before night. On the morning of the third all started on a review of the third corps, and the cavalry, in the vicinity of the Antietam battle ground. After getting through with Gen. Burnside's Corps, at the suggestion of Gen. McClellan he and the President left their horses to be led, and went into an ambulance or ambulances, to go to Gen. Fitz John Porter's Corps, which was two or three miles distant. I am not sure whether the President and Gen. McC. were in the same ambulance, or in different ones; but myself and some others were in the same with the President. On the way, and on no part of the

The text in President Lincoln's handwriting of the proposed answer to the *New York World*

> Abe may crack his jolly jokes
> O'er bloody fields of stricken battle,
> While yet the ebbing life-tide smokes
> From men that die like butchered cattle;
> He, ere yet the guns grow cold,
> To pimps and pets may crack his stories. . . .

It was felt that if this story went unchallenged a great deal of harm would be done the President in the coming election, and his friends appealed to both himself and Marshal Lamon for public denial. In a letter from A. J. Perkins addressed to Marshal Lamon following the appearance of the *New York World* story of September 9, 1864, the matter was declared to be critical.

President Lincoln on the twelfth of September sat down and wrote out an answer for Lamon to send to Perkins. Lamon was to copy this, affix his own signature, and send it out as his version of what actually happened and as a denial of the story published by the *New York World.* After writing the script, however, President Lincoln decided that it should not be sent out, feeling, as he stated, that the people knew him well enough not to believe such accounts of unfeeling conduct on his part.

Below, and on the facing page, is the Lincoln text in his own handwriting, photographed from a facsimile now in the possession of William H. Townsend, well-known Lincoln historian and collector, of Lexington, Kentucky:

battle-ground, and on what suggestion I do not remember, the President asked me to sing the little sad song that follows, which he had often heard me sing, and had always seemed to like very much. I sang them. After it was over, some one of the party, (I do not think it was the President) asked me to sing something else; and I sang two or three little comic things of which Picayune Butler was one. Porter's Corps was reached and reviewed; then the battle ground was passed over, and the most noted parts examined; then, in succession the Cavalry, and Franklin's Corps were reviewed, and the President and party returned to Gen. McClellan's Head Quarters at the end of a very hard, hot, and dusty day's work. Next day, the 4th the President and Gen. Mc visited such of the wounded as still remained in the vicinity, including the now lamented Gen. Richardson; then proceeded to and examined the South-Mountain battle ground, at which point they parted, Gen. McClellan returning to his Camp, and the President returning to Washington, seeing, on the way, Gen. Hartsuff, who lay wounded at Frederick Town. This is the whole story of the singing and its surroundings. Neither Gen. McClellan or any one else made any objection to the singing; the place was not on the battle field, the time was sixteen days after the battle, no dead body was seen during the whole time the President was absent from Washington, nor even a grave that had not been rained on since it was made.

"The little sad song" referred to in the letter, Lamon says, was "Twenty Years Ago." He said that this, above all others, was the President's favorite, that no other song so touched his heart, and that he was often moved to tears by hearing it. Marshal Lamon says that Judge David Davis, Leonard Swett, and Judge Corydon Beckwith were equally partial to it. Lamon had frequently sung it for them when they rode the Illinois Circuit together. Lincoln especially liked the lyrics and Lamon lists the sixth verse as one of those he liked best. Surely it was Ann Rutledge who came to his mind when he heard Lamon sing "I thought of her I loved so well," and he must have remembered with regret "those early-broken ties" which had so saddened his recollections of the old days in New Salem.

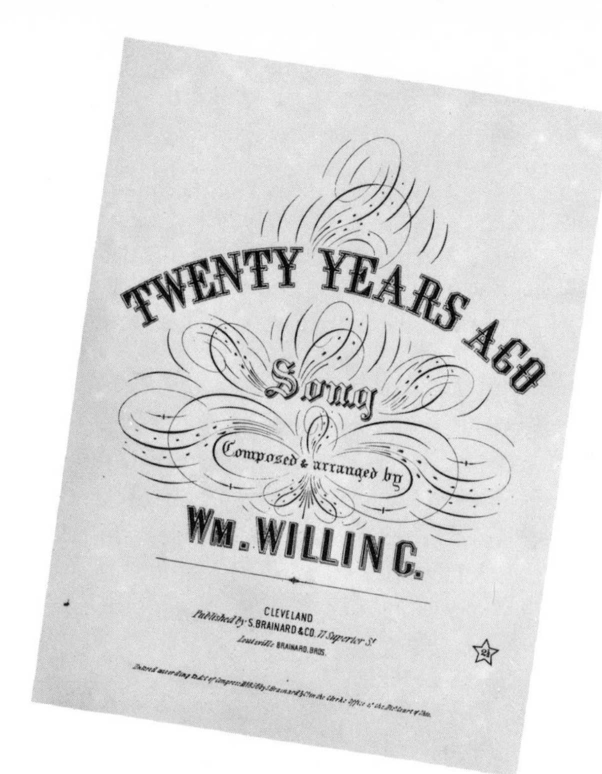

2

The grass is just as green, dear Tom, barefooted boys at play
Were sporting just as we did then, with spirits just as gay;
But the Master sleeps upon the hill, which, coated o'er with snow,
Afforded us a sliding place just twenty years ago.

3

The river's running just as still; the willows on its side
Are larger than they were, dear Tom, the stream appears less wide;
The grapevine swing is ruined now, where once we played the beau
And swung our sweethearts "pretty girls" just twenty years ago.

4

The spring that bubbled 'neath the hill, close by the spreading beech
Is very low; 'twas once so high that we could almost reach.
And kneeling down to get a drink, dear Tom, I started so
To see how much that I was changed since twenty years ago.

5

Near by the spring, upon an elm, you know I cut your name,
Your sweetheart's just beneath it, Tom, and you did mine the same;
Some heartless wretch had peeled the bark, 'twas dying sure but slow,
Just as that one, whose name was cut, died twenty years ago.

6

My lids have long been dry, dear Tom, but tears came in my eyes;
I thought of her I loved so well, those early-broken ties;
I visited the old churchyard, and took some flowers to strew
Upon the graves of those we loved, some twenty years ago.

7

Some now are in the churchyard laid, some sleep beneath the sea,
But few are left of our old class, excepting you and me;
And when our time shall come, dear Tom, and we are called to go,
I hope they'll lay us where we played just twenty years ago.

We may assume that with President Lincoln's insatiable love for music of all kinds, and especially singing, he or his close friends would see to it that every performer of note was honored with an invitation to appear at the White House. One who enjoyed such an experience was Adelina Patti, who in later years wrote of her visit there.

Mr. Lincoln had noticed her great talent when he had seen and heard her as a child prodigy of eleven somewhere at a concert, and he had followed her career with interest. She visited the President and Mrs. Lincoln soon after the death of their son, Willie. She says that she at first felt ill at ease in invading their grief, but soon forgot her self-consciousness in singing for them. She noted that the President was especially touched by her singing of "Home, Sweet Home," probably the greatest "Home" song ever written and, strangely enough, the work of a man who was homeless practically all his life and who found his grave on a foreign shore.

Glanz un_sern Sinn,........ Doch im _ mer zieht Sehn_sucht zur Hei_math mich
though we may roam,...... Be it ev er so hum_ble there's no place like
hin......... Den Reiz, den die Hüt _ te der Hei _ math ent _ hält,........ ihn
Home!.... A charm from the skies seems to hal _ low us there..... Which
beut, so ent_zück _ end kein Ort auf der Welt. Hei- - -
seek thro' the world is ne'er met with else_where Home!
pp
math......... süs _ ser Laut, wie klingst du lieb und traut,......... wie
Home!...... sweet, sweet, Home! There's no place like Home!...... There's
klingst du lieb und traut!..........
lento
no.... place like Home!...........
colla voce
pp
ff
ten.
ff

2. Wenn fern.... von der Hei' - math um - sonst winkt das Glück;........ O
express
2. An Ex - ile from Home Splendour daz - zles in vain!........ Oh!
p
gebt..... mir mein Dörfchen, mein Hüttchen zu - rück........ Die Vö - gel so
give.... me my low-ly thatch'd Cottage a - gain!...... The Birds sing-ing
traulich einst lock.... te mein Ruf;...... O gebt mir die Hei-math, die....
gai-ly, that came.... at my call...... Give me them with the peace of mind
all mein Glück er - schuf. Hei - - - math...... süs - ser
dearer......... than all. Home! Home..... sweet sweet
Laut. Nichts gleicht der....... Hei - math, Nichts gleicht der Hei-math traut!
largo
Home! There's no...... place like Home!...... There's no.... place like Home!
p
colla voce
pp
ff
ten.

Another singer, Lillie De Hegermann-Lindencrone, has told of singing for Mr. Lincoln, who complimented her performance, saying, "Music is not much in my line but when you sing you warble yourself into a man's heart. I'd like to hear you sing some more." She then sang for him "Mary Was a Lassie," and he added, "I think I might become a musician if I heard you often, but so far I know only two tunes." She jokingly asked if one of these was not "Hail, Columbia," to which he agreed, saying that he remembered it because he had to stand up and take off his hat when it was sung. Asked about the other of the two songs, he hedged by saying that it was the one where he didn't have to stand up. Knowing his love for and interest in and knowledge of many songs, we can recognize here the man of the world engaging in complimentary small talk with a public entertainer. In part it follows his pattern of always denying any musical ability whatever, and often in a manner implying that he didn't know one tune from another.

William Hardy Crosby, still living in Chattanooga, Tennessee, has an interesting story in connection with Lincoln's favorite waltz. Mr. Crosby's daughter was married to Joe M. Herndon, a relative of Lincoln's law partner, William H. Herndon.

Mr. Crosby tells me that his great-uncle, Lamon Crosby, left his old home in Staunton, Virginia, and moved to Springfield, Illinois, establishing residence there some years before the beginning of the War between the States. Abraham Lincoln was beginning to be a political power and Lamon Crosby, his warm personal friend, became one of his ardent supporters, in spite of their marked differences of opinion on certain matters. Soon after the outbreak of the war he became a spy for the Union army and remained in active duty until the close of the conflict.

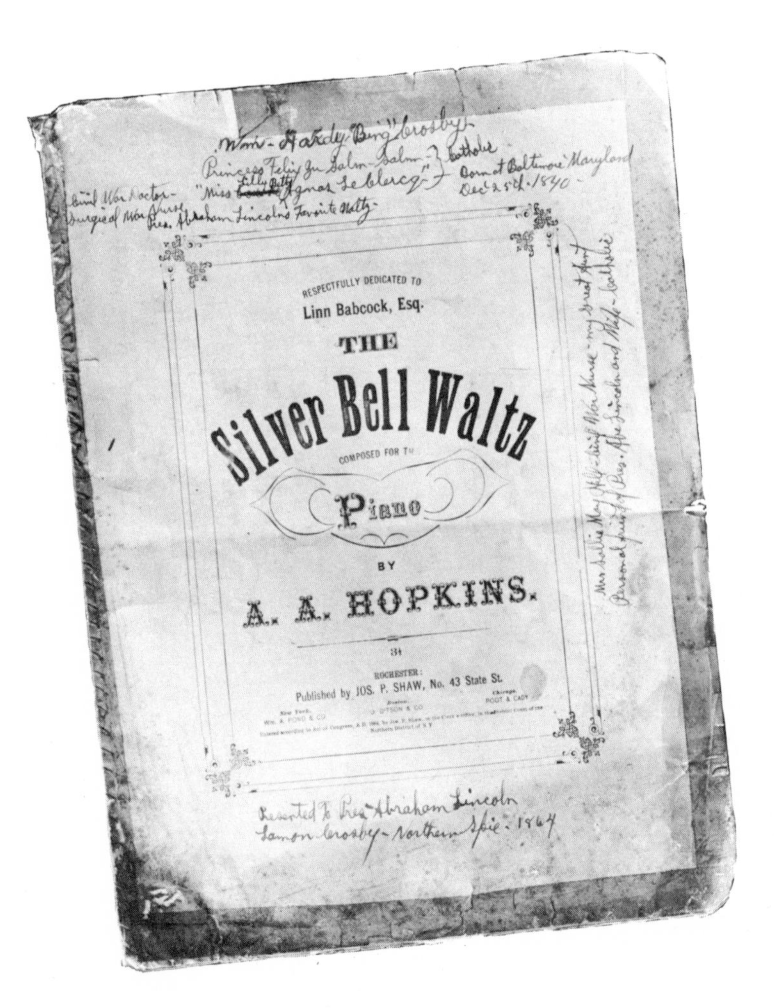

His brother, James Crosby, grandfather of my informant, had remained in Staunton and had gone into the Confederate service in the capacity of veterinarian, being in charge of all their horses for the whole territory between Staunton and Lynchburg, Virginia. He was captured by Union troops and spent thirteen months in a federal prison. But his troubles did not end there. Livestock valued at $18,000 was taken from him by General Hunter and never paid for.

Lamon Crosby, in his capacity as Union spy, was sent into Virginia to estimate the strength of the Confederate army and draw a map showing the disposition of their forces. Doing his work under cover of darkness, he was hidden during the day in the barn on his brother's plantation, as remembered by William Hardy's father, James E. Crosby, who was six years old at the time. He said that when he would go into the barn he would see his Uncle Lamon, hidden in the hayloft, who would jokingly tell him that he must not stick a pitchfork in him when he went about feeding the old cow which was the only animal left on the plantation.

Lamon Crosby escaped detection and came through the war uninjured. His operations as a spy were so successful that he was credited in the files of the War Department with having furnished much of the information that enabled General Grant to force the surrender of the Confederate army at Appomattox, and he was present on that memorable occasion.

Knowing President Lincoln's liking for music, he had, during the latter part of 1864, presented him with a copy of "The Silver Bell Waltz," later quoting Mr. Lincoln as saying to him that it was his favorite waltz. After the assassination of the President early in the following year Mrs. Lincoln returned the piece of music to Crosby.

"The Silver Bell Waltz" is here reproduced from the copy once owned by President Lincoln and later returned to Lamon Crosby, by whose descendants it has been preserved.

SILVER BELL WALTZ.
Composed by A. A. HOPKINS.
Allegro.
f
Ped.
*
p
8va
ff
Entered, according to Act of Congress A. D. 1864 by J. P. SHAW, in the Clerks Office of the U. S. District Court for the Northern District of New York.

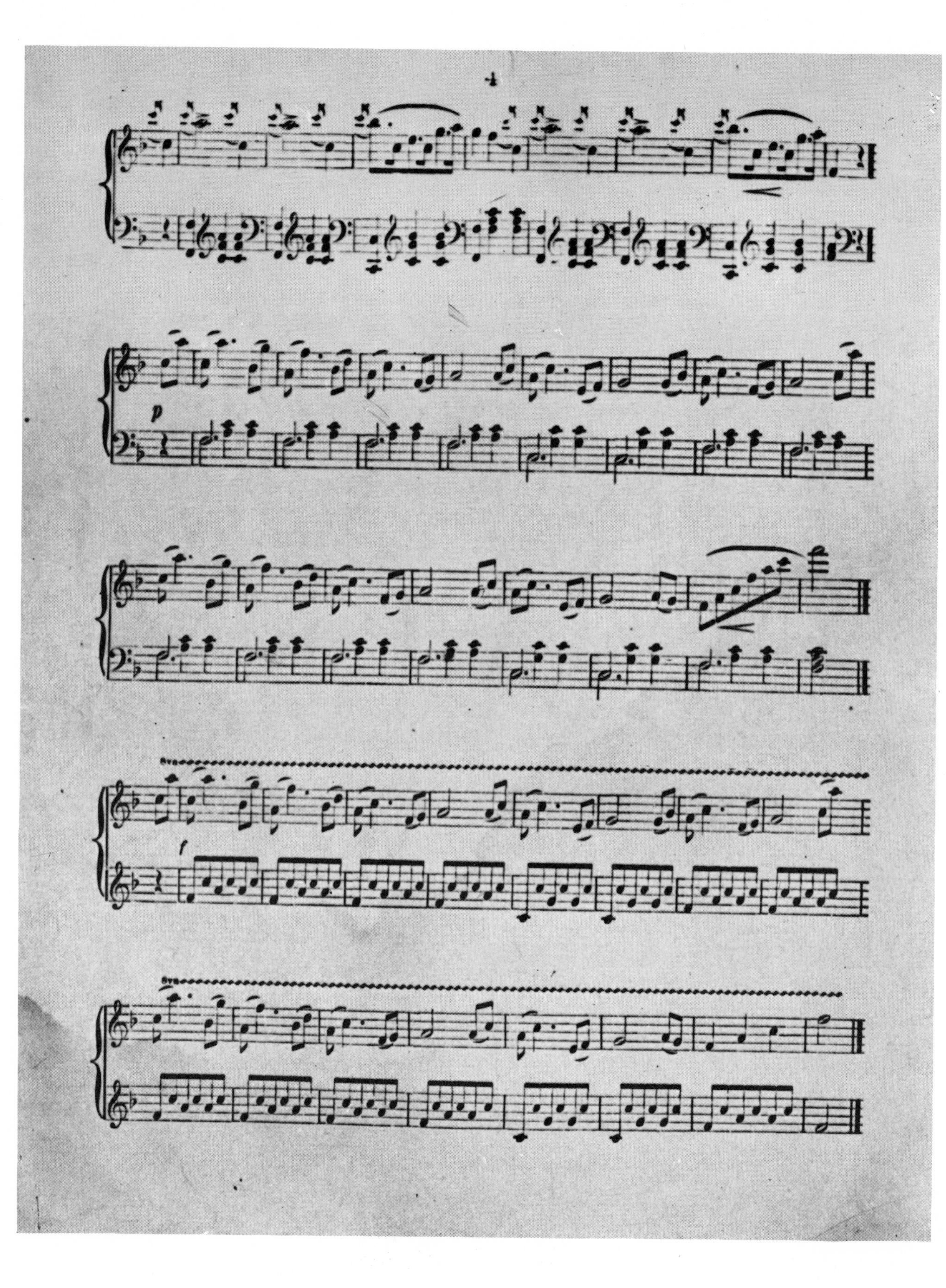
p
8va
f
8va

5
p
Ped.
p
ff
ff
dim.
ff
cres.
fff

"LORENA."

Poetry by REV. H. D. L. WEBSTER.
Music by J. P. WEBSTER.
VOICE.
PIANO
Andante Espressivo.
3. We
4. The
1. The
2. A
loved each oth-er then Lo-re - na, More than we ev-er dared to tell; And
sto - ry of that past, Lo-re - na, A-las! I care not to re-peat, The
years creep slowly by, Lo-re - na, The snow is on the grass a-gain, The
hun-dred months have pass'd Lo-re - na, Since last I held that hand in mine, And
what we might have been, Lore - na, Had but our lov-ings prosper'd well— But
hopes that could not last, Lo-re - na, They lived, but on-ly lived to cheat. I
sun's low down the sky, Lo-re - na, The frost gleams where the flow'rs have been. But the
felt that pulse beat fast, Lo-re - na, Tho' mine beat fas-ter far than thine. A

5

Yes, these were words of thine, Lorena,
They burn within my memory yet;
They touched some tender chords, Lorena,
Which thrill and tremble with regret.
'Twas not thy woman's heart that spoke;
Thy heart was always true to me:—
A *duty* stern and pressing, broke
The tie which linked my soul with thee.

6

It matters little now, Lorena,
The past—is in the eternal Past,
Our heads will soon lie low, Lorena,
Life's tide is ebbing out so fast.
There is a Future! O thank God,
Of life this is so small a part!
'Tis dust to dust beneath the sod;
But there, *up there*, 'tis heart to heart.

It would be impossible to bring together in one volume all the songs Lincoln knew. As this work has progressed it became increasingly apparent that not even all those for which he was known to have a preference could be included within these pages. Notable among those omitted are "The Sword of Bunker Hill" and "Tell Me, Ye Winged Winds," which Lincoln's friend and biographer, Charles Carleton Coffin, tells us was a favorite of the Springfield days. He states that this was the song Mr. Lincoln heard being played and sung as he passed a home in Springfield one evening; Lincoln was so impressed with it that he asked for and received a copy of it from the young lady who was singing it. "The New Jerusalem," said to be a favored hymn with Lincoln, runs to thirty-one verses and has not been included here.

Abraham Lincoln's life, and particularly the last twenty-five years of it, fell within a period when sentimentality was engulfing American culture and producing such songs as would most naturally appeal to a man of his feelings. Then, too, Negro minstrelsy was still in full flower and we may be sure that at one time or another he heard all the songs incidental to that type of entertainment.

As he advanced in the world and moved about in the larger centers of population he must have heard all the songs of the day, including those of Stephen Collins Foster. We know he was acquainted with "Gentle Annie," but in my opinion the "Pore Old Ned" which Dennis Hanks said Lincoln tried to sing was not the same as Foster's "Old Uncle Ned." Dennis speaks of the period prior to 1830, intimating that he and Abe went their separate ways after that date. Foster did not write "Old Uncle Ned" until 1845 and it was not published until 1848, at which time Lincoln was in Congress or riding the Circuit and out of touch with Dennis. In my boyhood in the Kentucky hill country I sometimes heard a song of which I remember this verse:

Pore old Ned, pore old Ned;
Slept all winter on a corn shuck bed.
Two at the foot, two at the head
And the one in the middle was pore old Ned.

I do not assert that this was the "Pore Old Ned" which young Abe Lincoln tried to sing but I have never found another song that better meets the requirements.

During his presidential campaigns and all during the war years many songs were written about, or dedicated to, Mr. Lincoln. Of these he would have especially enjoyed hearing "Old Abe Lincoln Came out of the Wilderness," as sung to him by his two small sons. Lincoln Memorial University, at Harrogate, Tennessee, owns a remarkable collection of such songs. Delving into it, with the able assistance of Mr. McMurtry, I came across a song entitled "God Save Our President." Scrawled along the margin, in an unidentified handwriting, was the penciled notation, "This song was sung at President Lincoln's first inaugural." Another, "A Dirge," carried on its cover the printed statement that it was sung at the consecration of the Soldiers' Cemetery at Gettysburg, November 19, 1863. Surely the President thought highly of these.

Mr. McMurtry also showed me a copy of a letter from Lincoln to George Fawcett, of Iowa, dated January 26, 1863, acknowledging receipt of a copy of "Emancipation Waltz." There was also a letter from William D. Brainard, in 1861, which had accompanied a copy of "Banner of the Sea," inscribed: "To Abraham Lincoln, with the well wishes of his friend, the author."

Here are reproduced the covers of some of the songs which would have been among his favorites.

"We're going to fight in earnest boys."
Abraham's Covenant
New Battle Song
Words & Music by
CHICAGO
WE ARE COMING
FATHER ABRA'AM
SIX HUNDRED THOUSAND MORE.
Composed and arranged by
PROFESSOR A. CULL.
NEW-YORK:
Published by HORACE WATERS, No. 481 Broadway.
Boston: OLIVER DITSON, 277 Washington Street.
OUR FLAG OUR ARMY
AND OUR
PRESIDENT,
QUARTETTE.
Words by
JAMES T. DUDLEY.
Music by
William H. Perry.
NEW-YORK,
HORACE WATERS, 481 Broadway.

God save our President
National Song
Words by
Francis De Haes Janvier
Music by
GEO. FELIX BENKERT.
BOSTON
Published by OLIVER DITSON & Co.

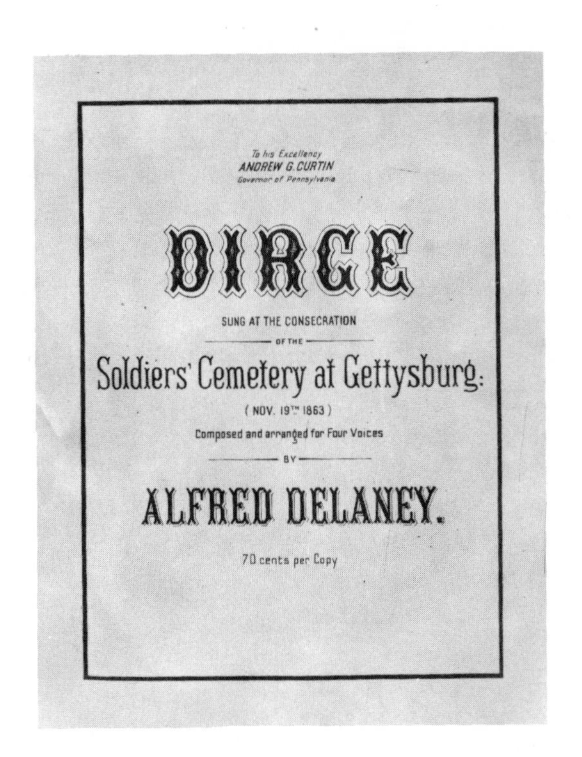
To his Excellency
ANDREW G. CURTIN
Governor of Pennsylvania
DIRGE
SUNG AT THE CONSECRATION
OF THE
Soldiers' Cemetery at Gettysburg:
(NOV. 19TH 1863)
Composed and arranged for Four Voices
BY
ALFRED DELANEY.
70 cents per Copy

On the morning of Friday, April 14, 1865, the management of the Ford's Theater in Washington was advised that President and Mrs. Lincoln and their guests, General and Mrs. Grant, wished to attend the evening performance of *Our American Cousin.* Immediate steps were taken to publicize the event properly; handbills were struck off and distributed and an announcement was prepared to be carried later in the day in *The Evening Star.*

The Evening Star also carried a news item to the effect that a new song would be introduced at this performance to honor Lieutenant General Grant and President Lincoln. The words, as given below, were by H. I. Phillips, a member of the cast of *Our American Cousin.*

HONOR TO OUR SOLDIERS

Honor to our soldiers,
Our nation's greatest pride,
Who 'neath our Starry Banner's folds
Have fought and bled and died.
They're nature's noblest handiwork —
No king as proud as they;
God bless the heroes of our land
And cheer them on their way.

Professor William Withers, leader of the theater orchestra, had set the words to music and obtained the permission of the stage manager to present the song between the first and second acts, sung by a quartet and backed by the entire cast. Had this plan been followed out President Lincoln would have had the pleasure of listening to a song dedicated, in part, at least, to himself, although General Grant was probably the one at whom it was principally aimed.

The ambitious composer, however, was doomed to repeated disappointments during the evening. The stage manager failed to spot the song as indicated, promising instead to put it on between the second and third acts. At the last moment he decided to use it at the end of the play, with Miss Laura Keene, producer and star of *Our American Cousin,* having a singing part in it. Those who are familiar with temperamental stars and harassed stage managers may form some idea as to why such changes were made, especially in view of the fact that Miss Keene herself sent a personal message to the President asking that he and his party remain for this feature. It was certainly not as Professor Withers had planned it.

It was this watchful Professor Withers who had been quick to interrupt the spoken lines in the play to lead the orchestra in the stirring lines of "Hail to the Chief" when the Presidential party put in a belated appearance some seven or eight minutes after the curtain had gone up on the first act. He had thus unwittingly been responsible for the last strains of music ever to fall upon the mortal ears of Abraham Lincoln. A little more than two hours after the President had listened to "Hail to the Chief" and acknowledged the applause accompanying it, the fanatical John Wilkes Booth, in his most theatrical manner, sent a bullet crashing into the brain of this man who had come a long and tedious way from the obscurity of a log cabin in the Kentucky backwoods to the height of national acclaim — from "Barbara Allen" to "Hail to the Chief" — a way sometimes brightened, sometimes saddened, by these, the songs Lincoln loved.

Hail to the Chief.

2 Ours is no sapling, chance-sown by the fountain,
Blooming at Beltane, in winter to fade;
When the whirl-wind has stripped every leaf on the mountain,
The more shall Clan-Alpine exult in the shade.
Moored in the rifted rock,
Proof to the tempest's shock,
Firmer he roots him the ruder it blow;
Mentieth and Breadalbane, then,
Echo his praise again,
"Roderick Vich Alpine dhu, ho! iero!"

3 Proudly our pibroch has thrilled in Glen Fruin,
And Banochar's groans to our slogan replied;
Glen Luss and Ross-dhu, they are smoking in ruin,
And the of Loch Lomond lie dead on her side.
Widow and Saxon maid,
Long shall lament our raid,
Think of Clan-Alpine with fear and with woe;
Lennox and Leven-glen
Shake when they hear again,
"Roderick Vich Alpine dhu, ho! iero!"

4 Row, vassals, row, for the pride of the Highands,
Stretch to your oars, for the evergreen Pine!
Oh, that the rosebud that graces yon island
Were wreathed in a garland around him to twine!
Oh! that some seedling gem
Worthy such noble stem,
Honored and blest in their shadow might grow!
Loud should Clan-Alpine then
Ring from her deepest glen,
"Roderick Vich Alpine dhu, ho! iero!"